CHANG

Changeling

A Memoir of Parents Lost and Found

SANDRA NEWMAN

Chatto & Windus
LONDON

Published by Chatto & Windus 2010

2 4 6 8 10 9 7 5 3 1

Copyright © Sandra Newman 2010

Sandra Newman has asserted her right under the Copyright, Designs
and Patents Act 1988 to be identified as the author of this work.

First published in Great Britain in 2010 by
Chatto & Windus
Random House, 20 Vauxhall Bridge Road,
London SW1V 2SA

www.rbooks.co.uk

Addresses for companies within The Random House Group Limited can be found at:
www.randomhouse.co.uk/offices.htm

The Random House Group Limited Reg. No. 954009

A CIP catalogue record for this book
is available from the British Library

ISBN 9780701182434

The Random House Group Limited supports The Forest Stewardship Council (FSC),
the leading international forest certification organisation. All our titles that are
printed on Greenpeace approved FSC certified paper carry the FSC logo.
Our paper procurement policy can be found at
www.rbooks.co.uk/environment

Mixed Sources

Product group from well-managed
forests and other controlled sources
www.fsc.org Cert no. TT-COC-2139
© 1996 Forest Stewardship Council

Typeset by Palimpsest Book Production Limited,
Grangemouth, Stirlingshire

Printed and bound in Great Britain by
CPI Mackays, Chatham ME5 8TD

To Sally

Contents

1

An Apparently Normal Human Baby

Prologue: Louise Elizabeth Oshins

She goes to a payphone first, she's walking through the parking lot where hers is the only car, Louise's shoes tick. It's a day so fine the blue, clean-cut sky amounts to a stamp of approval. Every decision is right on a day like this. I imagine her in thong sandals that smack her heels with each step; the thong between her toes is a comforting limit like a horse's bit. The pharmacy paper bag in one hand. She would be fierce, not crying yet. Louise dials her divorce lawyer, leaving a message saying she's committing suicide and where she is. He's playing golf all day that day, and no one gets the message till the following morning. That's what kills my mother.

She walks back to her Pinto, a pale-green compact car with bucket seats; my slim and sloe-eyed mother, her figure lovingly preserved at forty-two. Her skin got leathery during the hospital years, the medication years. She has a fixed ravenous expression, but Louise is still a pretty girl at ten paces. Shuts the door and everything is very still inside a car. It's like being zipped into a plastic bag. Tab was all she drank, the pink familiar can is a reassurance. The everyday implies a next day. I imagine she's crying now, a self-pity that feels like being loved, not enough like being loved.

Then it's happening, gulping pills with a practised gesture, three, three, three. They're red, sugar-coated, Parnate. Shaped like M & Ms. The carbonation buzzes in her mouth, it's going to be OK. It's autumn, bright weather, and the whole day stands round, a panorama looking down at the miniature car, not interfering, the glib blue sky.

Parnate overdose gives you low blood pressure, then you fall into a coma and die. Her forehead resting on the steering wheel, the pressure of the hard bowed plastic the last thing.

Too late, a man knocked on the car window to see if the sleeping lady was all right. He called an ambulance. My father came home red and sobbing, like a monster, wet all over. He stammered the news. I went to be alone, and lay down on the sofa in the living room that was Sears opulent – flocked wallpaper, gold plush upholstery. I lay full length, and I remember grief as a pleasant sensation of sleepy cold, of long-awaited relaxation; similar to the effects of Parnate overdose, or to the blissful release of finally completing a nerve-wracking, gruelling task with much at stake.

Background

I always knew I was adopted. We were told before we knew about sex; I don't know what the idea 'real parents' meant to us. I know it was one of the things that made me special, in my mind. I was left-handed, I was from the one Jewish family, and I was a changeling. To find out who I was was against the law.

I was adopted at thirteen days, and Sheldon and Louise were the stock nice Jewish couple, middle class, with a house in Massachusetts with a backyard and an upstairs. They were liberal politically; conservative in their domestic arrangements, avoidance of profanity, choice of friends. Just what anyone wants for parents, they were sweet people, people who made bad jokes and laughed like mad, who smoked and liked the beach, still in love from everything that I know.

My dad was an engineer for the government, developing radar systems, good safe money. He was from the West Side of Chicago. In a one-page stab at a memoir he once wrote, he described the gangsters on his street out shovelling snow. They waved to everyone, they seemed like perfectly nice people. That was what my father was like: everybody was nice, he saw the good side. Because his dad fixed cars, they weathered the Depression comfortably, and even owned a vacation cottage on Lake Michigan.

My mother was from the Bronx, and photos of her as a teen are like publicity shots for *West Side Story*; a pretty rangy girl in skin-tight pants, smoking, looking tough perched on the hood of a car with fins. Louise Oshins, a slanty-eyed knockout with a goofy grin and an hourglass figure – but Sheldon was the fat kid. Why did the knockout marry the fat boy? I asked my mother once and she said he was nice. 'No – why?' 'He was nice.' 'But, *Mom*.'

Sheldon was the common-sense guy, easy-going, not that ambitious, liked his food and didn't drink because he hated the effect it had on people. When a pretty girl walked by, he said, 'Hoo ha!' to the end of his days, he was unteachable on this point. Liked science fiction with corny jokes and smut, ideally Heinlein. He was not ashamed of being fat (three hundred-plus pounds); even when a chair broke under him during a meeting, Sheldon told it later as a funny story. He had to ask for a seatbelt extension when he took a plane. That didn't embarrass him. As he got older, Sheldon struggled walking, his legs inadequate to his size. It was like an enormous wardrobe being rolled on tiny castors. Never had any crazy dreams about what his life might be. Work was for money. Love meant marriage. When he came home from work, my father watched TV, every night of his life, and didn't want for more.

He was working class enough that he didn't know, growing up, that he was bright. He discovered that when he was drafted for the Korean War. He got the short straw: the Marines. In that war, the life expectancy of a Marine platoon leader in battle was sixteen minutes, making this turn of events commensurate with a diagnosis of terminal illness. Sheldon scored in the highest category on the Marines selection test, allowing him a choice of training. He chose electrical engineering school for being longest, eighteen months. Boot camp took time as well, so by the time my dad was ready to fight, his tour of duty was effectively finished. He spent his last few military weeks on Martinique, flying light aircraft and walking on the beach.

Sheldon had no attachment, then or ever, to bravery,

macho, glory. Though he worked for the Defense Department all his life, my dad found violence dumb. War topped the charts of dumb. And he was liberal in the blithe way of a man who assumes right-wingers are kooks. It was terrifying, Sheldon said, to meet the four-star generals. 'Suddenly you realised, this fellow's a – excuse my French – fucking idiot.' Serving an enterprise he found stupid and malign didn't worry him: working was for money.

He met Louise the year of his discharge from the Marines. She was nineteen; he was twenty-four and slim for him from two years in the service. A baby-faced man with a belly, his life was coasting into happiness; in the wedding photos you see his grateful cheer that things work out just right. They couldn't have kids, so they adopted. That was for Louise; all women wanted kids, kids were happiness. Louise was twenty-eight when they got my brother Seth. I came two years later.

Then everything was fine for a long time. It was the American dream, it was suburbia. The world smelled like cut grass.

And how people often put it, if a person attempts suicide on multiple occasions, is: *He killed himself five times. She killed herself four times before she made it.* It's an error that persists so stubbornly it's not an error but a perception. The insight must be that (my mother, of course this is all my mother) didn't live through those attempts, she came back from the dead. She came home from the hospital with death on her, unwholesome flesh, and she was never the same. She didn't smell the same.

It began when I was nine. And over the next four years, my mother killed herself six times, before she finally made it. She was in and out of mental hospitals. The last time, I was thirteen and Sheldon was divorcing her finally; to spare the kids.

I still remember her measurements, which she repeated like a mantra, so vain: 36–26–36. She had a mania for tanning. Louise brewed her own tanning oil because the brand name stuff wasn't strong enough. She was narcissistic, carping. Her conversation centred on her migraine headaches, minute shifts in mood, praise she had received. But I don't exactly remember her. I remember fear of her, not her. She was a bully, maybe. She was a 'bad mother'. She was doomed, it turns out, so I can't hold it against her. I remember that I loved her devotedly, to excess, but I don't remember what it was like.

My personality

As a child, I spent my free time in the woods, alone or with a comrade; balancing on logs, climbing trees, building forts that never stood. The New England forest was laced with creeks that froze in winter. You could walk along the milky ice, there were shapes like gnarled black lizards underneath. I had the firm belief I could discover a path into another reality (Narnia, Oz) so I kept looking. I was the ringleader, always daring the others to do the next, worse thing. It was I who insisted we take off our clothes in the woods, we crawl through the electric fence to get close to the horses, we run away from home.

When I was ten, my friend Sandra Jill Cameron told me she had made a remarkable discovery. There were microscopic animals that lived on sticks: giraffes, wolves, elephants. She, only she, had the ability to see them and communicate with them in English. By fiercely concentrating, I developed this ability too. We spent some weeks talking to the animals on the sticks, who told us many secrets about the past and future. Sandra Jill Cameron also discovered microscopic kings who lived in drawers. I remember going home alone one day and opening my drawer. I focused the force of my mind until I knew what the king was saying. I saw him in my mind in his yellow serrated crown, his poodle beard. He was foreshortened like a chess piece, which made his gait awkward; he made a rowing motion in his strenuous progress over my notebooks.

Then Sandra Jill admitted she'd been making it up. I cried and we had a wailing child-fight; I loved Sandra Jill

Cameron then with the purity of fantasy, with the daft, exquisite love of poems and dogs. She had betrayed my love and put the drab lid of reality back on the world. I would never get over it.

A week later I announced to two other friends that I, only I, could see and hear the voices of microscopic animals that lived on sticks. In the course of a recess period, they too developed the uncanny ability.

One day I discovered I could communicate telepathically with my midnight-blue ceramic marble. It said it was lonely, lonely; I went across the street to inform my friend Becky Briggs. I was ready to hatch a plan to release the marble's soul. She listened gravely, respectfully, before asking whether I was absolutely sure. I blushed, only then realising I was making it up.

I was always checking out books on extrasensory perception from the library, practising astral travel. You had to visualise a vortex and then allow yourself to be sucked in. Then you opened your eyes and the room stared back, absolutely unchanged.

At Becky Briggs's house once, playing (miserably, tediously, how can anybody be into this) Barbies, I drifted off, staring at the spines of her stacked board games: Trouble, Battleship, Monopoly! One, whose rules were too complex for it to be any good, was called The Game of the States; an educational game about the US map. I suddenly announced my real parents were named States: Mr and Mrs States. It was clairvoyance, I was so nearly certain.

And sometimes I said my real parents were Cherokee Indians, competing with Becky who was really one-sixteenth Indian. That was why we could both walk on top of the snow's crust without breaking through.

Louise

She's in bed with a migraine headache. The ice bag on her head is disturbingly brain-shaped. Dark blue with white stars. It has a screw-off cap where you put in the ice cubes.

I have to be there to keep Mom company. She kills herself because of the pain, it's migraines every day now. ('It's like I got a vice on my head.') She's had her thyroid cancer, too. It wasn't terminal; a cancer that grew so slow, the doctors said, it could have gone twenty years without threatening her life. Still, safe side, she had an operation. Then the radiation treatments made her all-day nauseous; and she got her tubes tied, despite her infertility. If she got pregnant after the radiation, the baby would be a mutant. When Mom comes home from her treatments, we aren't to touch her; she's radioactive. It would give us cancer, too. And cancer, radiation, mutants, are all ideas from a horror movie, things which can't be real.

I'm doing exercises on the floor, following instructions in her *Ladies' Home Journal* for the ideal sit-up. I clown, standing on my head, falling splayed to make her laugh. I chatter, 'Why are you depressed, Mom?' 'Because the migraines; it's like I've got a vice on my head.' And I ask her what it was like when she was my age, growing up in the Bronx.

So she tells me about the orange cat she had, Redrick von Ketchup. He climbed a telephone pole and got electrocuted, that was how he died. Louise was a smart kid, straight As; and her best friend was a girl named Shelley. Shelley like Sheldon, and I imagined my father telescoped into the frame of a child in a blue cotton dress. She had blonde curly hair of which my mother was jealous.

When I remember my mother at all, I remember fear and pity as the half-dark of pulled shades in a suburban bedroom. *Kojak* on a portable black-and-white TV; the flicker of black-and-white light on a quilted bedspread, on a TV tray. Going downstairs to fill her ice bag was a rite, like the exact execution of an OCD compulsion. Mom is going to kill herself but I am holding that time away as I go down the carpeted steps. I'm the one who understands. I can walk on the crust of the snow without breaking through, I can hear the thoughts of inanimate objects, I'm going to save her life.

My personality

My tenth birthday present was a manual typewriter. It had been my father's college graduation present in '58; for a couple of years, I'd been the only one to use it. A Smith Corona Clipper, it was 'portable' because it had a carrying case, though it weighed twenty pounds. I started writing books about animals escaping from zoos, or mustangs that had been rounded up but escaped through craft, or even stuffed animals that came to life and escaped from homes like mine.

My earliest extant work is a book called *Love's Magic Lands*; a novel handwritten on white lined paper with illustrations in crayon. It tells the adventures of a stuffed lion cub called Love. Love runs away from his owner and journeys through various fantastic countries – Babyland, Candyland, Plasticland. A green plastic lion cub called Lemon-Lime is his travelling companion. *Love's Magic Lands* was in its way a *roman-à-clef*: the heroes were real toys, belonging to friends of mine, that I passionately coveted. There were no human beings in *Love's Magic Lands,* or in any story I wrote as a child.

Animals were better than people. When I died, I would be a wolf, a horse, in my next life. People were gross; obscenely bald with skin like vinyl. I thought of them as having the squeaky smell of the vinyl seats in a new car. The sea was dying with poison made by people. And the trees were dying, the end of the world. I was going to run away from home and live in the woods, I was learning how from books.

I discovered an anti-vivisection ad in one of the magazines

I got from the library (*Horse & Rider, Arabian Horse World, National Geographic*). It described puppies undergoing surgery without anaesthetic, cats with bleach poured into their eyes. I reacted as if I had been told that the Nazi concentration camps had never been closed, they were still operating full-tilt and no one had mentioned this fact because it was normal to adults. I wrote an informational flyer on the manual typewriter and began to go round school asking the children to donate money to the fight against vivisection. I no longer remember why they didn't give; only my strange feeling of being mute, invisible, because I couldn't make anyone *see*.

There was another petition I wrote, against the real-estate development at the end of the street. They were going to cut down a patch of forest there, where we had our bike trails. I went from door to door throughout the neighbourhood, gathering signatures, but never did anything with it. I wouldn't have known where it should go.

And sometimes I remember myself as if I lived alone in our three-storey house; like a child in a whimsical children's book who inherits a three-storey house from an eccentric aunt. I lived on frozen pizza, ice cream, stayed up all night long. I don't remember my family being there.

Louise

We're at the mental hospital for the first time. We walk my mother, who is dead for the first time, lumbering and vacant, to the cafeteria. They're serving duck à l'orange: for the rest of my life, that dish is, in my mind, radioactive. (The sauce looks radioactive. It's what dead people eat. This is the world after nuclear war, the people walk like zombies.) As we sit, eating with harmless plastic cutlery, my mother says that she doesn't feel anything any more. She doesn't know if she loves us now. She doesn't feel love.

We're quiet, and I'm trying to feel the shape of this, like trying to sound out an unfamiliar word. It's the thing Moms don't say. It's the thing they said was possible just to scare you. Then my father says, 'Louise, you don't mean that,' helpless, angry. Seth and I are sent to the common room so he can speak to her alone.

In a mental hospital common room (later, one of dozens of trips, until it was like a family campground, it was where we went at the weekend) a patient taught me to play pool. I sank the orange solid first try, beginner's luck. The patient was over-eager, thrilled for me, calling me the champ, like a shy uncle. I remember puzzles I put together, idle hours spent cross-legged on the carpeted floor of those common rooms; a new form of waiting for grown-ups.

And American culture is suddenly all about mental illness: the seventies. There are TV movies and best-selling books with titles like *Diary of a Mad Housewife*, *The Cracker Factory*. Divorce is the other topic. I'm beginning to read my father's porn novels on the sly, and all these things are part of a growing warp in the nature of things. All afternoon

13

there are no adults at home, you have that freedom you always wanted but it's as if every sound you make is amplified, putting down a fork is deafening, you're so scared.

I was trying to love her more. I was always telling her I loved her, trying to feel the shape of what I said. It was easy to love the cat. I loved my brother Seth so much I hated him. Not her, I couldn't love her enough to make a difference, and trying left me with the feeling I had when I practised telekinesis and the paper clip would not move, though I knew the paper clip *must* move, and I entirely expected the paper clip to move, it didn't. And there was a *nothing happening* that was unnaturally intense, as if this was the first time nothing had happened since the world began.

Therefore

My mother asks me to get her a soda. I'm brattish, resistant, 'Mom. Why can't you get it yourself?' Still, I'm downstairs pouring it when I hear the crash. I run out, and Mom's at the bottom of the stairs, curled against the sideboard there, blood in rivulets down her face. The blood is shockingly liquid, live. You can see it move.

I remember calling 911 and knowing as I dialled the phone I'd done it before. I don't remember the other times.

'I asked Sandy to get me a soda, because I felt too sick to go, and she said no. When I went to get it myself, I fainted at the top of the stairs,' is what my mother says when my father arrives; her voice is weak, vague. She's lying on the gold plush couch where I will lie, released from suspense, when I get the news of her death. The lights are low, the paramedics are packing their equipment, embarrassed, not looking at us. I don't say anything. To object would be to break the run of luck that means she's alive. She only has a mild concussion.

But when the paramedics have gone, my father says, reserved with anger, 'Is that what really happened, Louise? Didn't you really do it on purpose, because you were mad at Sandy?'

And Louise begins to wail and admit that she threw herself downstairs. Because she killed herself because she really wanted to die – and to punish us. She killed herself to get out of going to a family reunion. She did it because she couldn't be our mother, we should leave her alone. She killed herself *at* us. And she would scream at us for failing

15

her, not caring enough. One night she feigned psychosis, asking me if I had seen my (non-existent) soldier friend, saying she heard bombs; just play-acting, she later confessed, to impress us with how sick she was. The night before the final time, the time she didn't come back from the dead, she'd taken Seth out bowling, and he'd said, 'I'm worried about how Dad's going to pay for our college if he has to pay alimony.'

And Dad said that was why she did it. She killed herself to make Seth feel guilty, Dad said; we were better off without her. By then I was an adult he could tell things, she was long dead, and he hated her. He never forgave Louise. He'd had a narrow path through life one person could ruin, and Louise had had no mercy.

I said to him, because I always defended my mother, 'But you have to understand, she was always in so much pain. It was every day like that.' My father said, implacable, 'Why? Why? There was *nothing wrong*.'

And I have a memory from being very small, kindergarten; the year we lived in Florida. In the memory, there's a tornado on the way, and I have to hurry inside to safety. I get to the screened-in porch of our house just in time. The storm is lashing, dry, against the screen. But it's a storm of spiders. Hundreds of spiders are landing on the screen, crawling over the screened wall and ceiling. The porch is blacking out with spiders. I take my doll and put it in my toy oven to keep it safe from the storm, and then I go inside.

My personality

Then she kills herself. I lie on a sofa and experience despair as peace. Everything's cold, but exquisitely quiet. I don't call anyone, I don't tell anyone. The next day the rabbi comes to the house to ask questions, gathering material for the funeral service. We struggle: she collected seashells, she loved Florida, she gardened, she liked cats. It's a series of mild surprises; Louise had a personality, she was a woman who collected seashells, she wasn't a disease at all. For the same reason, these factual statements feel like lies. When these items recur in the funeral service, they come across as an argument in favour of Louise still being alive.

She's cremated offstage, we never see any body, coffin, evidence. At the funeral, they bury a small shiny box. If it was a gift, perfume. Folding chairs on the grass, bright autumn weather. A dragonfly pauses on my knee, as if singling me out.

My father guides me to the rental car and says he'll be right back. I get in the back seat and, shutting the door, it's over. I'm in the gentle spell of air conditioning. Nothing bad has ever happened to me in this car. On the drive home nothing can happen. It's the enchanted peace of liminal space; how airports, taxis, and the few blocks' walk between the bus stop and your destination can become a sanctuary. Then there's a knock on the window.

It's Louise's father, Grandpa Alan. Through the tinted glass, he looks strange in his black suit; like a man who works in an office. I've rolled the window halfway down before I see he's uncontrollably weeping. He thrusts his hand through the window and seizes my shoulder.

He says, choking and rushing the words, as if any moment he might be swept out of reach, 'Remember Grandma – always remember she loves you.'

Then he's gone. I'm crying as if I'm crying Grandpa's tears. When at last I roll the window up, the car's spell of safety is broken. It's now the car in which that happened, in which I don't know what sickening thing just happened. I don't know why I'm crying yet.

I never see him again. My grandmother has ruled that Sheldon is to blame for Louise's suicide. She will never speak to Sheldon, or to my brother and me, again. Her husband and my mother's sister go along with the excommunication as a matter of course.

2

Where Parents Come From

Ida Oshins

Nowadays, a doctor might diagnose Louise with a chemical imbalance. In the seventies, there was one source of mental illness and one source only: the patient's mother.

Handily, Louise's mother was a tyrant, a figure of fear. A black-haired, sour-faced woman in a house dress, Ida radiated evil. She ran her family as a cult of punishment. Every word, act, facial expression, was examined for the taint of disobedience. Her punishments were frightening not because she broke any bones, but for their vehement cruelty. For instance, Louise never liked to eat, as a child was squeamish of even chocolate. In the canonical story, her mother made her eat a breakfast she had already vomited once.

Louise's father, Alan, was a downtrodden, silenced man, a bony pauper type with a shy demeanour. That he was a mailman is an example of life's grim wit; no other walk of life could better suit his air of being trounced. His wife terrorised him; the dinner conversation turned on Alan's failure; he carried a mailbag in the rain; dogs chased him. Instinctively kind, he endured Ida's viciousness to their children in harrowed silence. In my memories, he stands beside her like a mute shadow self, a Dorian Gray grotesque representing Ida's withered conscience.

For his wife, Alan changed his name to Oshins from Oshinsky. The children all got goyish names; Louise, Paul, Bernadette, because his wife was too good to be a Bronx Jewess; too good to be a mailman's wife. The youngest child, Bernadette, was blonde, therefore her mother's favourite. From Louise's point of view as a child: Bernadette, not she, got ballet lessons.

The son, Paul, was banished from the family eventually for marrying a Catholic girl. Though the Oshins weren't religious, his mother had forbidden it. Paul lost his mother and father and lived happily ever after. After the rift, Louise went on visiting Paul – at my father's insistence. Paul's treatment by his parents made Sheldon indignant to the marrow of his decency-loving Midwestern bones. 'Your uncle should be free to marry whoever he wants. Ida just couldn't stand him loving anybody as much as his mother.'

Louise was the eldest, and the scapegoat. She raised her brother and sister single-handedly and got short shrift. As an adult, Louise led with, 'Well, I'm sorry I can't do anything right,' ferocious, teary-eyed. She was working on her insecurity, her sarcasm, her self-hate. And it was like trying to eradicate genetic illness from each cell of one's body, one cell at a time. Meanwhile, new sick cells grew in, and there was Louise; the absurdly full-grown unloved child. To oppose her mother turned Louise's psyche inside out. Although she loved Paul with the double love of a sister/nanny, she once attempted suicide rather than go through with a planned visit.

And Ida had a male best friend, Albert, a businessman she went on holiday with. A lover, I guess, though no one used that word. And these were the exotic fruits of an era in which divorce was stigmatised. And this is all family lore, the fragments parents tell their children before those parents' untimely death.

The moral of the story was that Ida was evil. There was nothing to understand about her motives – she was evil. Ida was an ultimate cause.

From the top: understand me this time

Ida married at nineteen and raised her children in a mouse maze of Bronx apartment buildings filled with shtetl Jews and their wild poor kids, in the years when the Holocaust was happening, taking place in real time; words becoming laws becoming hunger and becoming human sacrifice in its twentieth-century form. The old country relatives became a sea of pleading letters arriving at New York brownstone apartment buildings where Ida's contemporaries were impotent, tiny with poverty in their dirty hungry ark.

Because my family didn't lose anyone they knew – only great-aunts and second cousins no one had met in person – the Holocaust vanished from family memory. The Depression vanished from memory. They became things that had happened on television. Like good Americans, we acted as if world history was a decorative backdrop. So history took the role of God the Creator, what makes us while remaining anonymous, invisible; something in which our grandparents believed.

When Ida was fourteen, the Great Depression began. She was seventeen when Hitler came to power. A few years later, the first death camps were opened; then the US entered the war. And the world of Louise's childhood was a few blocks long and wide paralysed by history.

There was the gnawing angry despair of the college-educated doing sweatshop labour to the end of their lives; and the different anger of young men living a drunken vendetta of street fights, guns, and robberies. American anti-Semitism was taken for granted; Jewish girls wore crosses to look for jobs. The men planned revolutions while children slept four to a bed, litter-style, in the next room. A generation lost its faith; their Bible was the daily newspaper. Their religion was Adolf Hitler, an anti-Messiah who had come at last for the Jews. Prayers to God would be trivial, irreverent, like a poetry reading at the foot of a mountain of corpses. Jews feared the extinction of the Jews until they longed for it; they had another drink and predicted the extinction of the human race.

Such things children must not know, but always know in a magnified, funhouse-mirror, way; as if they'd learned the news in dreams. Hitler could be a demon, an alien monster. One of a child's imaginary lands would have been the Thousand Year Reich, where people are put into 'ovens'. People are turned into soap and lampshades, as by a witch's curse. At last the evil is banished by a bomb that destroys a city at one blow, a finale for a Bible story.

Newsreels at the time showed graphic images of both the enemy and the American dead. There were interviews with the pilots of the Enola Gay, elated after the successful mission. The children would have watched clips of the liberation of Auschwitz, waiting for the cowboy feature in the clothes that children wore then: simple dresses, short pants, duck-bill cloth caps – the same clothes their cousins wore as they boarded the cattle-cars to Auschwitz/Birkenau.

And Louise had an orange cat named Redrick von Ketchup. He got electrocuted running up a telephone pole; that's how he died. Her best friend's name was Shelley: a girl who had blonde Shirley Temple curls of which my mother was jealous. These were the only things Louise would tell me about her childhood.

I make it all right

You could let go and blame nothing. Nothing human could be alien to you. You could grow into the girl who sleeps with anyone who seems to need cheering up; you could live in a world where everyone's naked and the dishes don't get done. Go ahead and sleep on the floor; flick your ashes on the floor, it doesn't have to matter. You could be raped and go to breakfast with the rapist after, and laugh about the misunderstanding. You could try to provide forgiveness enough to make up for all the blame in the world.

She makes it all right

You could let go and blame everything. You could remove every threat of pain from the world through heroic vigilance. You could abolish the class of people who think they have the God-given right to cause you pain. Cross out the son who doesn't care about you; erase the grandchildren who are sour reminders of the daughter who died to spite you. You could even live out the few dreams available to a mailman's wife in the Bronx; the married lover and the hotel beds; the Jersey Shore vacations that make life pass, that make it possible to bear the vicious solitude.

A penultimate death

At the family conference at which the divorce was announced, my father presided. We were in the living room, convened on the love seat, rocker-recliner, and the formless couch – chummy furniture meant for watching television. Because we'd never had a family conference before, Seth and I had already guessed its subject. All that remained to be seen was how well they would put it across; like watching a production of Shakespeare with an amateur cast.

The wallpaper had a stain-resistant sheen, and was a bracing red-orange plaid. The furniture was a dissenting brown-blue plaid, and the carpet red shag with a texture like rough yarn. A framed embroidery portrait of a kitten hung on one wall; a seascape in oils, with eyebrow-style gulls, bought from a Cape Cod sidewalk, on another. The decor gave the scene a fundamental silliness – like dying, as some people must, in a McDonald's.

Dad began with an account of our harrowed lives, a blur of used-up noise amounting to a ritual, a makeshift Kaddish. We were told, as children are accustomed to be told, that this was for our good. Translated, this meant we had no say in the matter.

When he reached the word 'divorce', my mother spoke up. She was tearful, she used her weak voice. And in that last year of her life, Louise seemed waxen, uninhabited; her short haircut had something clinical about it. The nostrils were over-emphasised because the eyes had dulled, were like matte plastic. Her tears and tantrums had become involuntary twitchings of an organism; ugly, meaningless spasms.

This was what we were meant to call 'Mother', and

cherish with our unconditional love. A ridiculous, insulting demand; an eat-the-breakfast-you-already-vomited task Seth refused to attempt, for which I now respect him.

Anyway, this was the Louise who was talking; not the lissome, goofy beauty who'd lived in the hard-knocks Bronx, and not the Mommy of memory who'd put Bactine on our skinned knees, but her remains. And she sat forward awkwardly, leaking tears, and murmured that she might move to Florida, after she got out of the hospital. She would stay in the hospital a few weeks, we could still see her. She would keep her promise to take Seth bowling.

'I love you just as much,' my mother wound down, dull-faced, evasive. Then she looked at my father as if for permission to leave.

My brother and I began to relax. The scene was losing impetus. Soon we could escape to our hiding places; put on the Led Zeppelin, watch *Fantasy Island*, call up friends to talk about anything but. Since Mom wasn't spending the night – she was on day release from the hospital – the worst was probably over.

But at the last moment, some rogue element in my father broke ranks. He turned away from Louise decisively, and announced to me and Seth, 'You know, Louise hasn't slept with me in months.' He paused, and his jaw set in pettish righteousness. He said, 'I have needs, too.'

It took us a moment to realise our father was referring to sex. Then – I don't know about Seth – my heart skipped a beat. I was torn between admiration and horror, violently quickly – like a startled cat that tries to run in two directions at once.

At last, Seth said, 'That's great, Dad. Tell us all about it.'

My mother said. 'Shelley, please,' and began to cry again, demonstrating her rote, trite pain.

I didn't say anything, until (Oh my God, he was grossly obese, was the unspoken thing I was thinking as Sheldon glared there in stolid righteousness. At thirteen, I was prepared to believe this was why my mother killed herself. Every other explanation, anyway, had worn thin from use. But another, occluded, part of my mind was fighting the sure conviction that my father was divorcing Louise not over sex, but because of my own first suicide attempt, the shallow cuts I had made in both my wrists in a fury of impotence, a week before. I had needs, too, but he should have known I didn't. I had needed to save my mother.) I said,

'Is this over yet? Can we go?'

This is over with, yes

• My mother killed herself because her mother mistreated her. She never got over her mother's small-time, squalid cruelty.

• It was the fallout from the Holocaust, the Great Depression; world history cast a long bad shadow into even the tiniest nooks.

• My mother had a neuro-chemical imbalance; Prozac would have done the trick.

• My mother killed herself because Seth said the wrong thing at the bowling alley, teaching him a lesson for all time.

• She did it because my father divorced her, dreaming of getting laid, some day.

• She wanted to get laid, worse, but she was married to a circus-grade fat man. She didn't have the nerve to leave her kids, house, faithful husband, and Louise malfunctioned, throwing out sparks from the sheer frustration of the beautiful unfucked.

• I killed my mother by cutting my wrists, the perfect crime.

• No one cares any more why my mother killed herself. And no one will ever know why. It is like the causes of World War I, if no one cared about the causes of World War I.

Then my family is over. My mother is a tasteful box buried in a plot with no stone and no visitors. My grandparents vanish, it was all a bad dream. Sheldon, Seth and I live in a three-storey house. Each survivor chooses a storey. My father doesn't climb stairs easily: he is the ground floor. My brother has the top floor, and, as the junior member of the family, I get the basement. We avoid each other for four more years before I can officially drop out of school and leave home.

Then I'm living in London.

3

An Alien Artefact

I decided to move to England because I fell in love. My father had taken me to London on a business trip. He was attending a three-day defence technology conference. For years I carried the freebie briefcase he picked up at that conference, printed with the comical/alarming logo *Military Microwaves*.

One afternoon of that visit, I went to Hyde Park alone and fell into conversation with a good-looking thirtyish ice-cream man. I fell into bed with him, and fell for him, and moved to London, one two three. I was seventeen.

I never saw the ice-cream man again. But I discovered a ravenous need for separation, for no associations with the past. Once in London, I was not just unwilling but afraid to move back home.

How I ran out of money: Sheldon gave me $1,500 to last my first three months in London. It wasn't enough to live on, but I could have asked him for more, all things being equal.

With the $1,500, I started by buying a poodle puppy before I even left Massachusetts. It was a poodle that looked like a mutt. I partly got it because I felt sorry for the dog, which had an ungainly bravura, for being a poodle. I decided it would be company, since I knew no one in London. At the last moment, I found out about the six months quarantine imposed on animals entering the UK. A friend took the puppy back to the pet shop. The money was not refunded, however, for several months.

My next purchase was a vintage car. The night porter at the hotel where I first stayed had a Hillman Minx for sale. It was a beautiful machine; grilled like a baleen whale, with a sperm whale's boxy outline. It could start with a crank, as well as with an ignition key. I only dared give half the price, enough for a first instalment. The car was towed before I took possession. By then, I didn't have the fee to get it out of the lot. The night porter couldn't pay either, so my sweet car perished.

I gave my remaining money to a man who claimed he needed it urgently for an investment opportunity. He would pay me back with interest Monday, said the extraordinarily handsome Italian man, Roberto, who fucked me twice before disappearing for good. I wasn't surprised. My feelings weren't hurt. I'd just thought it would be vulgar to be suspicious. I didn't care about anything as grubby as money; I wasn't like Roberto.

Having nothing was going to be an adventure. It would be like running away from home.

I decided to become a prostitute because it was immediate. I'd run out of money so abruptly, and I had to eat. I had to pay my rent. Men were always calling to me from cars in West London then, and police sometimes mistook me for a hooker, too. I had the habit of pausing on a sidewalk, staring into space, wool-gathering. Something about it helped me think. Men would shout from cars, 'Do you have a place?' or even, 'Do you need a fix?' The cops would move me along.

They were narrow streets of expensive flats and cheap

hotels. Yellow lamplight lingering on the edges of the cobble-
stones; a light rain as if the city is reaching out to touch
you, superstitiously. The man would pull his car up, window
rolled down. 'How much, love?'

The fucking felt like minor surgery under local anaes-
thesia; a distant tugging, scraping feeling while my body
wanted to tense and squirm away. It kept wanting to. It/I
wanted to lash out, fight, and keeping still took all my
will. I was trying to enjoy the feeling because I badly
wanted to be liked at that age. I knew to enjoy the sex
would make me liked.

You had to hold still and make pleasure noises. I practised
the noises in my spare time. I used to try contracting my
vagina like I'd read in books, and also practised this,
although I was never convinced that anyone noticed.

Some men said they loved me, as if I couldn't hear. Sometimes, I got sore until my vulva stung like an open blister,
and I began to cry a little, from weakness and self-pity. The
preoccupied johns never mentioned it. They never showed
they noticed; it was like being an animal handled by a bored
vivisectionist.

Everyone said I wasn't the type. I used to be silently
outraged because they thought someone was the type to
scrub their toilets, empty their garbage, suck their cocks in
the front seat of their cars for £15 in cash. Several men
told me the recent tabloid story of a prostitute who'd been
chopped up and found in various parts of Brighton. I
couldn't understand what made them say it; it amounted
to 'I could kill you.'

And I used to carry a single-edged razor in my pocket.
I had used one as a twelve-year-old to cut my wrists, I'd
always liked them. It was a sharp blade you could buy at
a chemist's for pennies; and a comforting object to hold in

your hand, make-believing you could win that fight, again and again, while you walked.

On the other hand, one kind Irish tourist mailed me an extra £30 from Dublin, although he wasn't even coming back to London. Another man, seeing how poor I was, dropped by to give me pots and pans. A homeless woman once walked me to my working street, commiserating, because she had noticed my air of fear and frailty. It happened to a lot of girls, she said, never mind, things would look up. I think I loved these people more than I have ever loved again.

One month I was a call girl, trying to move up in the world I had. I worked for a madam, going to Mayfair hotels to fuck rich Arabs. The madam still turned tricks herself; a louche and gorgeous thirty-something, she had gone by her *nom de lit* so long she had begun to absent-mindedly call all people by her former name. Even the cat was given her old name.

I only worked for her three times. The last time of the three, I was with a client named Omar. It was late afternoon; Omar and I were sitting side by side on a leather couch in a hotel suite. On a second couch sat one of Omar's business colleagues and the colleague's elegant Arab girlfriend. Omar was smoking a hookah and wearing a long white nightshirt garment. The men were speaking in Arabic. Everyone was seemingly in a good mood, though I was like a fly on the wall in that a fly on the wall wouldn't understand human speech. I didn't know anything: what country they were from, what anyone did for a living, why Omar wanted a prostitute here in the middle of a business meeting.

Their clothes, their hair, the room and all the furniture were perfect. Every smell was planned, was a perfume. There was no dust, dirt, lint. The room was huge, and every millimetre so pretty it made you want to fall asleep, it was like a relief.

Then Omar, without altering his impassive expression or speaking to me, reached to my hair and pulled my head down toward his lap, pulling up his skirt to reveal a naked erection. I sucked his dick in front of the business colleague and the elegant girlfriend. Omar continued smoking his hookah throughout. I remember it having something resembling a sleeve of uncompleted knitting covering the hose; my head was under this knitting, part-concealed. The scene is lit in my memory with the screechy over-brightness of traumatic experience; operating theatre light, imbued with malice, so that even the room-service French fries I ate cold when the others had left and Omar had fallen asleep were each one a contamination, a gratuity accepted from a depraved kingdom of rape. Yet very little had happened. It was only that Omar didn't seem to know I could see and hear, that if he'd shoved his finger through my eye, I would have felt pain. These are simply impressions. But I gave up that job, went back to working the street, fucking ordinary guys who would talk too much and act embarrassed – *You shouldn't be doing this, pet, you're not the type, it's dangerous* – although street work paid a pittance, it was £15. And it was probably dangerous.

The reason I left prostitution was that I was raped.

One day my friend Ben, a fellow student at the Polytechnic of Central London, was sitting with me in a low-life café we used to waste hours in in Soho. A low-life sat down with us and started to tell lies about a shoplifting ring he ran. He said his name was Mick: he was a short burly man, Sicilian dark, a red-hot raconteur with an operatic contagious laugh.

Ben and I, down on our luck, excitedly said we'd shoplift for him, given the chance. Mick took only me – I don't remember how this happened – in his car to scope out jewellery stores. Rather than bringing me back in fifteen minutes, as he'd said, he only brought me home the following day. Rather than going to jewellery stores, he drove me straight to his flat in a distant, unidentified part of town.

'I just remembered, I said I'd meet this bloke at two,' Mick said. 'It's a money thing, love. Come up for a minute.'

I baulked, and we were bickering at the entrance to Mick's apartment block, when the bloke came walking up. Cash changed hands. Reassured, I agreed to go upstairs for a minute, and we ended up lounging, drinking wine, then tea, then wine, on his sitting-room couch until late night. Mick kept putting off driving me back. It was one more drink, and just one more; then he had to sober up to drive.

By 2 a.m., he was telling me his life story. He'd hated his old man, who had terrorised him, who named him Spit; Spit was his legal name. When his father had died, he didn't feel a thing. Only went to the funeral just to please his mum. He'd rather burn than be a dad like that cunt. He showed me Polaroids of his children, four and six, on Santa's lap. Baffled-looking black-haired children with a wife from whom, Mick said, he was amicably divorced. Still had a pint together Sundays, sure they did. She wanted to move to Cornwall now, though, silly cow. He didn't know what he'd do without his son and daughter, he guessed at my age I wouldn't . . .

Then he began to wrestle with me. At first I didn't take it seriously. But by the time he forced my legs open, pulling aside the crotch of my panties, he was swearing at me; leave off, you bitch, leave off. I was crying and swearing at him under my breath.

While he raped me, I scratched my own arms deeply, raising welts to distract myself. It worked, I remember the scratching clearly now and not the rape. I remember an emotion that made the scratching seem like fingers down a blackboard, and I remember the rough-and-tumble feel of wrestling. Not rape.

I remember being in the bathroom afterwards and thinking of books I'd read in which a raped girl needs to take a bath immediately. She feels polluted. That's how DNA evidence gets lost. I wanted to kill myself, but washing seemed absolutely irrelevant. The idea of evidence with its train of police and prison was grossly irrelevant. Men get raped in prison, who could do that to anyone deliberately.

When I came out, Mick looked hangdog. With a cautious, cajoling air, he said that he'd truly believed I wanted it. I blurted out, 'How could you think that? That's ridiculous.'

Then we bickered, as if we were old friends.

And he offered to get me work as a heroin courier, to make it up to me. I said that was fine, cool. I didn't see any reason to be unpleasant, to cut off my nose to spite my face. And I even showed up for the meeting Mick set the following day, because I didn't have next month's rent, and I couldn't do prostitution any more, it was too much like getting raped, and if I didn't pay the rent, I might end up in the street, and get raped. My thinking had narrowed dramatically or it had stopped being thinking. Of course Mick didn't show up.

'I'd like to give your father a piece of my mind,' the night porter who sold me the Hillman Minx, who became a friend, used to say. 'Young girls should have nice things to wear. They shouldn't be wearing old T-shirts and living in grotty depressing bedsits and eating nothing but Cup-a-Soup. You never eat anything but that Cup-a-Soup, do you? There you are! You tell him I said that.' And later, 'You're not the type who should be offering herself to sleazy Kuwaiti gentlemen in the streets of Bayswater. You're too sensitive. You're terrified of people, aren't you? That father of yours should give you money! You're not going to tell him, are you?'

But how could I explain to Sheldon that I'd thrown his money away on a poodle, a vintage car, and an Italian con artist, none of which were now to be found?

It all had a happy ending, or at least an anticlimax. My friend John Muckle – whom I'd been in love with all this time, but who had a girlfriend he was faithful to although she wasn't always faithful – kissed me. Two weeks later, he took me in. John Muckle became my first real boyfriend, and I moved into his tower-block flat in Acton with bleak views of all Ealing. John taught me myriad things of daily utility: how to make chips and slice bread; the differences between Leninism, Trotskyism, and Stalinism; why no right-thinking person rated Martin Amis or Neil Kinnock – how to be a citizen of London's numerous contrarian class. I made friends, and in a pinch I could sleep on those friends' floors and couches; I had the perquisites of a citizen.

Meanwhile, my first three months in London had expired. Another $1,500 came. It was that simple; it had been that brief. It could be encapsulated as the story of how I learned thrift.

Still, for years, I could never meet a person without guessing whether they were like the Irishman who sent me £30; or like the men who fucked me while I cried, getting value for their money.

Lifestyle, eighteen to twenty-five years old

Always broke. After John Muckle and I broke up, couch-surfing. Taking milk and sugar in coffee to make it a meal; scrounging fivers. I couldn't hold down a job, too afraid of people. I did a BA at a polytechnic, badly; my four-year course took six years. Sheldon continued to send me money, enough for rent or food. I spent it on cigarettes. The reasons he wouldn't give me much: I should have held down a job, and I should have come home to a cheap state school. It was all true, I was sorrier for him than me.

Not a useful daughter: Sheldon of all people didn't owe me a living. On visits, I would listen to his quotidian troubles, we'd be having this kindly conversation. Then I'd snap and couldn't stand the sight of Dad (morose, a mass puddled on a chair, a collared shirt in J.C. Penney cloth, the innocence of his ageing face), the thought of his thoughts.

I smoked two packs a day and wore one change of clothes. Triumph motorcycle T-shirt, leather skirt. When I was nineteen, I fell ill, 'chronic fatigue syndrome' or hysterical collapse. I was weepy sick like having the flu for three years roughly.

Solitary like a hand-shy dog, I couldn't just talk to people. I got tongue-tied, tried too hard. Pressed, I made deliberate gaffes. If I'd slept with a guy, I relaxed, I thought he'd cut me slack. I fucked a lot of people, it meant something different then, like helping someone on with their coat. Like asking someone what they thought; a cordial overture.

There were good times naturally. There were calms in all those storms like being washed up on the idyllic beach. Your friend would make you cheese on toast and laugh at your joke, and it was like some heroin that was sugar, like floating in sex, just to be liked; so good no one ever felt that way, you were superhuman with love. It was a mystical experience of watching television in a council flat.

Then back to walking in the rain with a fever and a suit-case. Arrive at the address (my friend said to stay the night, it was cool) shaky, dizzy with gratitude; I ring the bell, and no one comes. The house is as silent as a solid block of wood. Twenty pence is all I have, I've lost my footing into weakness, panicked. When I try to lift the case again, I can't. I can but. I could if I could beat self-pity, its vampirism, but I'm too weak to stop the damn self-pity. I'm swooning from it on the wet November step, stuck like the dead leaves plastered to the concrete step like starfish, nowhere to go. I hit the bell again, no hope now – but there's the door opening, my friend spun into being like a frowsy genie, drunk; I'd woken him up and I apologised, I fervently apologised because I couldn't do life right, and I was honestly sorry.

Initiating event: the phone rings

I'm in the States on a visit, wasting a day in the former rec room Seth took over as a teen. Then, his bedroom was off-limits to me; it has the virtue now of no associated memories. The waterbed's gone, but the centrefolds and Confederate flag still hang, making it a sort of Seth Adolescence Memorial Room. I've been in London seven years, and I'm in my final year at polytechnic; twenty-five years old.

I'm lying on the floor, chain-smoking, desolate, staring at a mariachi made of bottle caps on a dust-rimed shelf. I'm needing and needing to leave, from the kind of home-sick where you can't bear being home, home makes you sick. I'm alone in the house.

The phone rings.

The phone rings more. At last I sit up, facing the bottle-cap mariachi, scared. The phone's rung like eight times now and I've got to get the fucking phone, in case.

I pick up and say disappearingly softly, freaked, 'Hello?'

A breathless girl-voice speaks. 'Hello, I'm calling from the Crittendon Home for Unwed Mothers. Could I speak to Sandra Newman?'

'Yes. I mean, I'm Sandra Newman.'

'We have reason to believe your birth mother is looking for you.'

It takes me a minute to put it together: the stranger improbably calling me here, the Crittendon Home, birth mother. Then something happens – as if the magnetic poles have switched inside me, and my self flips backwards in my body.

Of course this is the agency from which I was adopted. It has never seen fit to change its quaintly Puritan name, which I have never known. I feel an immediate keen nostalgia, a grief that I was robbed from there. I could have been content among Unwed Mothers, in a Home outside suburbia, parents, school. (Later, when I meet my own unwed mother, this grief will seem like prescience; she's exactly the wayward, hapless waif, more sinned against than sinning, my imagination painted.)

I say, 'My birth mother got in touch with you?' elated past any possible shyness.

'Not quite,' says the woman, abject. 'We made a mistake.'

The mistake was unwittingly giving my name and address to a private detective. He was posing as a hospital official, claiming that files had been damaged in a flood. The Crittendon receptionist, gullible as an unwed mother, said, 'Of course, I'll look that up for you . . .'

Then somebody realised, too late. They managed to call the detective back, and he confessed to not being a hospital. He wouldn't give his client's details, though, not being scatterbrained like them.

I say, 'Oh, that's OK. I don't mind. I would be happy to meet my birth mother. If she should call . . . tell her.'

The woman gives me the detective's contact details, affectionate with relief. Miraculously, they aren't going to be sued.

Three months pass

At last, I can't stand it any more. Although it's showing weakness – like being the first to call after a date – I write to my birth mother via the private detective. I tell her the basics about myself, but, making myself sound good. That is, cutting out the major events, and concealing my real personality.

Another two months pass before I get a letter back.

White business envelope

The letter says:

he's my father, not my mother.

He's a poet and novelist. He lives in LA with his wife, an art curator. My father has three other children; two sons and a daughter, all a few years younger than me.

When he met my mother, they were college students. They were together just four months: they were already on the rocks when she got pregnant. He hasn't seen her since before I was born.

When he knew her, my mother was beautiful and 'intellectually brilliant', doing a degree in Russian. (When I report this back, my mother is deeply flattered. She immediately phones to repeat the compliment to her old friend Frank, the one she stayed with in the last days of her pregnancy, now a microbiologist at MIT. He guffaws and says, 'Don't worry. You're *not* intellectually brilliant.')

The letter is cordial but concise. Its tone bespeaks my father's business background. It comes in an ordinary white business envelope, addressed in fountain pen. The graceful handwriting of the address suggests a decorous, faintly eighteenth-century character – a personage. It makes me imagine my father at a rosewood desk, dipping a pen into an inkwell, while a deerhound naps at his feet.

And the letter gives me a feeling of improbable, abracadabra joy; what angels feel, or the children of happy families feel. It's a species of happiness new to me; as if I'd first tasted chocolate as an adult.

Dear [my real father],

I'm sorry I've taken such a long time getting in touch; your letter found me in the last week of writing a BA dissertation which more or less swallowed my life for several days (also why I have no typing paper). 'Issues of Time in The Sound and the Fury'. *I think I've come out of it well, as I can still read Faulkner, although I no longer have any concept of time whatever. Which should be enough excuse-making.*

I would be happy to get in touch with you. I can re-assure you that I haven't been terribly damaged or confused by being given up for adoption (I hear a lot of adopted-child horror stories about people who commit suicide when they find out they are adopted, or else never speak to their adopted family again, or at least lie in bed for two years drinking and listening to Leonard Cohen records). My (also adopted) brother and I were told that we were adopted as soon as we were old enough to understand it. I have, in fact (I hope this is not tactless), always enjoyed being adopted. Certainly at eight years old or so it is the essence of glamour, and all of your little friends envy you. Your parents really aren't *your parents, at a time when everyone else is helplessly wishing that this were the case. It did spoil that changeling fantasy for me (I never, I don't know why, sat around thinking, maybe my mother is the Queen of England and she is looking for me). I do remember once experimenting with telling my friends that I was really the child of aliens, who communicated with me at night.*

I don't know how far the private investigator got with investigating me, how much you already know about me.

I specifically couldn't tell from your letter whether you already know that I am a Russian student (it's actually a joint honours Russian/English BA, a peculiarity of the college I go to). To make the coincidence still more funny or pleasurable or frightening, I also write (some poetry but mostly a novel of – currently – 200 pages) although I have never published, or tried to publish, as of yet.

What more can I tell you, for openers … I have been living in London for about six years now, currently in my college's halls of residence. I am unmarried; no children.

Could you send me a snapshot of yourself and possibly a representative poem? I'm enclosing (which I guess you have already found) a photo booth picture of myself.

I had just as well to sign off now or it will never get to the mail –

Hope you are well –

With all friendly consideration –

Sandy

Two months pass

When I got the second letter, I'd finished college, with the result that Sheldon stopped sending money. I was living in a squat, though, so my expenses were low.

I shared the squat with three men: Will Jakeman, Richard Jones, and Amos Weisz. I had then just married Amos, though we didn't share a room. We were opposed to intimacy, which we found bourgeois to the point of being faintly Viennese. Plus we couldn't stand someone being there. A passport marriage between lovers, it turned all too genuine, too love-wrung. 'Marriage, despair, and death,' Amos muttered, on the way to buy the pawnshop rings; that was the first warning sign he was taking it seriously. I was insulted. It amounted to accusing me of marrying him. Once the fear took root, it came true.

Will Jakeman and Richard Jones were Amos's old friends; also my ex-boyfriends. They were opposite kinds of ex. Will doggedly, cheerfully, tried to sleep with me every time we spoke; while Jones had vowed to never speak to me again. The situation was complicated by the fact that Amos and I had an open marriage.

My squat bedroom was a litter of papers, books, dirty clothes, and the plates from my last several meals; like Will's and Amos's rooms, and the hallways, and the stairs. Due to age and warped floorboards, the carpets were uneven as rocky ground, and the same variegated brown. I had no furniture; I slept on a row of sheepskin rugs. In one wall, I had driven dozens of nails from which to hang my clothes. My manual typewriter sat on a pallet from a building site. All life's activities took place on the floor.

It was 1991, and a monkish Socialism prevailed in London. The only extravagances condoned were illegal drugs and promiscuity. To pay one's bills was collaboration with the enemy. Success was déclassé, and being on the dole the stamp of a serious artist. But to live near the centre of town still had cachet; the craving for a posh address is probably hard-wired into the brain. Our squat, being in Islington, was a London anarchist's dream home.

There were superior squats, of course: Mayfair squats; or squatted pubs and derelict cinemas. For one heady week some of Will's friends squatted the Iraqi Embassy, after Iraq's diplomats had been expelled from the United Kingdom. Coming from friends' settees by way of the poly halls of residence, though, I had precipitously risen in the world.

Scene begins

An ordinary white business envelope appears on the squat front hall's cracked lino, landing amidst the bills we never opened, never mind paid. Picking the letter up, I get that swoopy impossible love; as if I am receiving correspondence from heaven.

I tuck those feelings away swiftly, superstitiously, and tote the letter to my room, like a dog solicitously fetching a newspaper to myself. In this period of my life, I only feel entirely human when alone. And it often happens, as I shut the door behind me and open into privacy, that I belatedly realise my pre-human, public self did something reprehensible, for which I will atone with hours of self-recrimination. But this time I just go in and sit down on the sheepskin rug and breathe.

I'm sitting Indian-style. It's pretty wonderful to have this father artefact. I open the envelope.

It contains a single-page letter and two photos.

When I'm done with the letter, I stretch out flat on my back for a while with my cheek sideways crushing down the spongy fleece. It's a joy as if the room is drunkenly spinning. I'm looking through the wavy sheep hairs, gold white beige. My life is growing exponentially although I just lie in the dirt, having nothing.

Through the wavy tawny sheep hairs, blurred with proximity, I focus on a book splayed open-armed on the carpet, and reach without thinking as if catching at a ledge to stop my fall. I drag it in and start to read.

The Brothers Strugatsky

In those years, I mainly read in Russian. This was to improve my Russian vocabulary – but also because it was a private language, like a tongue concocted in the throes of a schizophrenia, but in which one then finds an eerie compendious literature has been written. In those days only a handful of Russians had got to the West. Londoners often didn't know what alphabet it was. I read Chekhov, Dostoevsky, Tolstoy, the stock great works. But my standby was the science fiction of Arkady and Boris Strugatsky.

The novel that day was *Beetle in an Ant Farm*. Subtly mutated human babies have been deposited on earth by mysterious aliens called 'The Wanderers'. Alongside the infants is an artefact inscribed with symbols that correspond to symbols printed on each mutant's elbow. Human scientists give the mutant babies to foster families in distant galaxies, to separate them from the artefact. The artefact, the scientists worry, might activate the mutants as Wanderer spies.

The babies grow into seemingly normal men. At a certain age, however, each is inwardly compelled to journey across the universe to the institute where the Wanderer artefact is kept under lock and key. The mutants perish, one after another, struggling to reach the artefact. At last only one is left.

What will happen if he gets to the artefact?

Will he change into a superman, a monster?

Will he signal an invasion?

At the crucial moment, the human characters panic and shoot the mutant just before he reaches the box where the artefact is stored. Then they stand around sadly discussing the amazing things they might have found out, if they only hadn't lost their nerve.

I pick up an alien artefact. It's one of the photographs my father enclosed with his letter, a photo of his three children. They're dressed up for some family event, a bar mitzvah wedding reunion like my family never had. The teenaged boys in perfect suits; my sister at fourteen in a sailor dress. The conservative clothes suggest a social world I not only don't inhabit, but have never visited: *National Geographic* exotica. Even the jauntiness, the ease, with which my older brother grins at the camera is something I associate with cinema, with, for instance, Tom Cruise.

They look like me. They could have been derived from me by a computer graphics program. Or I could be averaged out from them: my sister's round-faced cuteness, with the darker severity of her brothers factored in. It's jarring: all this while I had supposed I was myself, an irreducible identity. No, I was a point on a continuum, a value.

There's a reflex of denial – as if I'd received a photo of myself committing a crime. *I wasn't there, I have no idea what happened, I have never been to Los Angeles in my life.* And I feel that, as long as we're doing science fiction, I should be able to summon them instantaneously by pressing a button. I want to. I want to touch their skin and see if I blend in.

Will knocks on the door. I'm on my feet before he finishes knocking. 'Come in!' I say, all over-excited and sounding it.

'What's that?' he says walking in. I hold the photograph out.

Will facts

When I was living with John Muckle, Will Jakeman moved into our spare room. Will was studying for his accountancy exams, coming home from his rookie accountant job and boozing while he memorised tax law; Captain Beefheart on the stereo and *Question Time* on the telly and Will would talk all through it. I was chronically ill with my then malaise, too shy to speak to even the flatmate. Nineteen in a mini-skirt and bad thick make-up (one French gay guy who hated me called me the 'Bébé Whore', I was like that) I'd be there suffering over Marx or some incomprehensible Scots prose poetry and never saying anything, all dark looks. I smoked, drank Diet Coke, and never ate. Will and I were natural friends although we just tiptoed around each other at first, alarmed, what is this alien phenomenon? At last a mutual friend told Will I liked him, breaking the ice. John Muckle was an editor then; he'd be out having dinner with authors because the Muckle was creating the Paladin poetry list while Will and I got stoned at home and watched *Eastenders*. It was like poor Muckle just had two teenaged kids.

Inevitably finally Muckle left me for someone better, and closer to his age (thirty-one), Nice Claire who edited children's books. I was jealous, inconsolable, too aware he'd made a smart choice. (Once Muckle visited me in my new place; in the course of telling some story about his youth, he said, 'But that was when I was just a colt.' I said, 'And now that you're a full-grown gelding?' We both laughed like crazy, mainly the note of 'woman scorned' made it funnier and we shared a moment of appreciating our dumb predicament as an aesthetic object. It was my first taste of adult sadness; when you can say of your devastated hopes, 'Yes, ouch,' and everyone laughs and you feel relieved because you don't have to matter.) Will, anyway, was one of the men I slept with in that heartbreak. Then we became that kind of friends.

Will had read Classics at Cambridge and came out with that hallowed Oxbridge badge and a drinking problem. He went into accountancy as a fuck-you to his lefty friends: his squatting and speed-fuelled pranks were a fuck-you too to the City gits. Will would crack a squat at night, sleep on a blanket on its concrete floor, then put on a suit and go to work at an asset management firm. He'd developed a taste for bare bulbs, washing in cold water, hotplates. He'd call in late to work, explaining, 'I got chucked out of my squat,' to piss them off, too young to really need money anyway.

In gaps between finance jobs, Will worked as a bicycle courier; chopped the suit trousers into pinstripe cut-off shorts. It was an old anarchist-run firm we all worked for sporadically; you'd hang in the office or down the pub, waiting for a job with the other couriers, bleached and pierced punk/rave kids smoking roll-ups and arguing about the Cathar heresies. Everyone was stoned and half were junkies, riding through ridiculous London at some break-neck speed and materialising in an office reception in a shaft of endorphin light, the drugs all over you in the form of sweat. Some bored receptionist snapped at you, disdainful; you were the glorious insect, lord of opposite-land. Will prided himself on vomiting from his bicycle without slowing.

And he wore those cut-off pinstripes or some madly baggy, threadbare, cycling shorts he had; too young to look anything but god-like; blonde, broad-shouldered, a craggy masculine prettiness, and his muscularity, puppy energy, abrasive charm. He was, 'All it comes down to – have you got good mates? Cause everything else is crap.' His mates were 'glorious nutters', 'glorious cunts', or 'solid'. If one of them gave up drugs or had a kid, settled down somehow, Will's term was, 'He got fat.'

Girlfriends, when he had them, were too good for any of us; just beautiful, smart, and good. Like A-list actresses playing Will's girlfriend, and Will was then head-over-heels. 'Thing about Karla is her gentleness,' he'd say in a hushed ideal attentive love; 'The first time I saw her, what I noticed was the gentleness in her face; she's *lovely*.' He'd start cleaning up his act. 'I'm rejoining capitalism,' he'd say, which meant he was getting a temp job. A sensible friend, Dan Metcalf ('fat'), would give Will one of his cast-off suits and the accountancy lark would start again – studying for exams, the 'perestroika-ing' which meant less drinking. Will would start devising get-rich-quick schemes; a Moroccan exports store he'd start, a finance journalism career, an employment agency to place Czech computer programmers in City firms. Nothing came of anything: success would first mean giving up drinking. Soon the girl-friend left for greener, more appropriate pastures, found her male Nice Claire who Edited Children's Books, got fat. I'd go see heart-stricken Will and he'd put on Gram Parsons singing 'Love Hurts' and talk the heartbreak out. Then we'd often fuck, not always fuck but often. Just to lighten the load, to make our dumb predicament seem like pleasure-seeking, *joie de vivre*.

'I think love is just what gets you over the post-coital triste,' Will said, one of those drifting days. I said, 'No, you don't,' and we knew what love was, for a sleepy ecstatic minute. We loved each other, and you could see it there, like a ghost that formed in the air and you recognised the face. For a moment life stood still and let itself be seen, a smoky tiny squatted room that was better than 'real' love; shared misfortune was.

Will took the photograph, frowned at me, frowned at the photograph. 'OK, me dumb. Not getting it.'

'My brothers and sister.'

'I thought – oh!' He looked back at the photo and lapsed into all grins, muttering, 'Shit. Shit,' in sentimental overload. Then suddenly he surged forward, threw his arms around me, and lifted me into the air. I was laughing and going, 'Just spin me around then! Fuck off! Fuck off!' lovingly.

At last he let go, stood back and said, 'They look like you! That is gloriously fucked.'

'It's sick. Is it a little sick?'

'Not unless you fuck them. Are you going to fuck them?'

'I don't know, I have no conception of anything.'

'Don't. Oedipus. It makes you go blind.' He handed me back the photograph. 'God, I can't imagine that. What's that like?'

'What? Hang on.' I ducked to put the photo safe on the floor. 'I always wanted brothers and sisters.'

'Fuck off. Seth's your brother. Seth's lovely. I liked Seth.'

'We haven't talked to each other for years. He's like an ex-brother.' I picked up the letter and the second photograph.

'No, he loves you. Why'd he come to visit you in England, then? You're full of shit.'

'You only like him cause you have the same birthday.'

'Oh, I'd forgotten that. Bastard nicked my birthday. All right! Bin the cunt.' (Will and Seth were born the same day the same year, astrological twins. Their personalities weren't remotely alike, comfortingly, there was no need to take astrology seriously. I felt nonetheless that Will was a brother equivalent, like brother margarine; or even a new improved brother, less the things Seth might have mentioned and awakened the past.) 'Oh, can you lend us a fiver?' Will said.

'Here.' I poked him in the chest with the letter. 'A fiver, I think so. I'll see what's in the tin.'

'Wait, what's it feel like? The extra siblings.'

It had stopped feeling like anything. I said, tentative, 'Good.'

'Fuck off.'

'Well, when I first got it,' I reluctantly said, from a compulsion I suffered to be scrupulously honest in the face of questioning, 'it was euphoric, fairly euphoric. But it's also like being replaced by simulacrums. Perhaps there's a slight desire to exterminate the clones, from a fear that they're draining your identity.'

'Good to see you're having a healthy reaction, then. Well sick.' He took the letter and said, 'Oh, this is the letter. Right.' Then he had started to read. I got down on hands and knees and fetched my collecting tin from under a blouse.

Right livelihood

It was Honest Essie ('Honest' because she was supremely crooked; she later, legendarily, got child benefit for two kids by recycling her only child as identical twins) who got us working for the phoney cancer charity. Run by 'the Doctor', a dodgy Hasidic guy, it was collecting money to research the role of beta carotene in curing cancer. We'd go round pubs with official charity cans, saying, 'Collecting for cancer research? Collecting for cancer research?' It was nearing Christmas; people gave like sentimentality-maddened lemmings. The tins were security-sealed against intrusion; there was only a single slender coin aperture in the top, so you couldn't shake the money out – unless you inserted a butter knife in the slot, then the change came magically pouring down the plane of the knife blade and out of the shaken can (Honest Essie's innovation). When you did deliver a poor residue of change, to keep appearances up, you found a long table of bearded Hasids sitting round counting coins all day in a trance, it was like a Nazi propaganda film. 'Fagin' was on everyone's lips. Sometimes the Doctor would try to get the cuter girls of the collectors to appear in promotional videos; they'd go to cancer wards and get filmed talking to patients. But only the Australians were naive enough to do it.

It was the first job that I'd been able to keep for more than a week. Earning money seemed supernatural; like conjuring money from a hat. The fact that it was fraud did cause me spasms of guilt, but as an anarchist, I accepted those as part of working. Any work that benefited capitalism was wrong, meaning any job I could get was wrong, and I went through mental operas of guilt at every temp assignment. Each business letter contained some taint of historic injustice, which would set the agenda of my next hour of suffering while I continued typing, 'It has come to our attention your account is in arrears', feeling like a collaborator. Serving the Doctor was purer. It was selectively stealing the pennies the victims judged that they could spare. You had also made yourself absurd and contemptible, expiating as you went.

There was, finally, no need to dress for work, which was always a bottleneck; by the first Wednesday at a temp job, I was wearing Monday's clothes, making Friday a looming catastrophe. I'd be skint, walking an hour to work. Lunch was out of the question. My default state was having no money at all, nothing in my wallet but dried-up grains of stray tobacco. Due to all this, I always looked strikingly different from the other office workers; sweaty, unkempt, emaciated, like a hostage newly released from captivity. I was nonplussed by the riches of people who purchased antiperspirant, socks, or Kleenex. Part of me believed they should give that superfluous Kleenex money to Oxfam. A less acknowledged part believed they should give it to me. Enter the Doctor.

Will Scene continued (Will is reading the letter)

Now I'd begun to get a stream of coins – a tricky, intuitive operation like milking a cow or tickling trout. Knifing the can was addictive; every now and then a bright fat pound slipped out, or the friendly big hexagon of a 50p. Then there would be a thin slurry of pennies, or a frustrating back-up, the coins sloshing heavily in the tin but refusing to tumble down the slide.

Then I heard Will gasping. I looked up, saying, 'What's funny?' knowing what was. Will was hot pink with silent tremulous laughter. He held his hand out for the second photo. I gave it to him, and he buckled, gutshot by further hilarity. At last he straightened and managed, barely:

'Never.'

That set me off; we were both near wetting ourselves. It was transcendentally funny; the punchline to the world. Will looked around, making a point of seeing the squalor, and laughed still more, now cackling, forcing it. He said, 'Well done. I know you didn't do anything but, well done.'

The letter began by inviting me to visit in LA. My father named the siblings in the first photograph, left to right, and informed me, breath-takingly, that he had tracked down my mother. She would write to me separately. She was thrilled; she was living in Northern California; she was doing very well. She, too, would love to have me visit. The letter went on to abruptly, carelessly, mention that he lived in a castle. This was the point at which Will had begun to laugh.

The second photograph was an aerial view of the Hollywood Hills. By following the letter's directions, you could find the castle, a long white compound slung along a bristly California hillside. Built in the Spanish style, it had perimeter walls and towers, it had a guest wing, it was an actual fuck-you castle. 'Never.'

Will handed me the letter back with a subtle dent where his thumb had been, where he'd warped the paper laughing. 'Well, you've got to hate him now,' said Will. 'Or is that, you've got to love him? Oh, you need the money. Right, then! Love!'

I looked high-mindedly at him until he repented, and Will leaned against the wall, rebuffed, sheepish. He said, 'But you do need the money. Cause Amos is crap. He's a poet, fuck's sake.'

'I should be able to afford to have—'

'Morals,' said Will.

I said, 'Parents.'

'Fuck off! Parents! A pony, yes. Get him to buy you a pony, he owes you a pony, he abandoned you. You can't want parents. Take it from me, pony over parents. Voice of experience here.'

'You had a pony?'

'*And* parents. Pony's better.'

We paused and look into the middle distance, seeing ponies, parents, castles. (Will's father had beaten his mother; it was screaming and chairs flying when he was growing up. Will tried to defend her, and it was sordid, terrifying, it was like a Russian coming-of-age novel. Meanwhile, Will's mum wanted to act as if nothing had ever gone wrong. She attended Church of England services, she put doilies on the backs of chairs.)

And Will crossed his arms and asked me if I felt less implicated in my family's fuck-ups because I was adopted. He was one of those people who wish they were adopted.

Being adopted would free them from the damning fact of being made out of the people they can't forgive.

And I said yes, I thought it made me feel less implicated. Since I didn't know who my real parents were, all I knew was, these adopted people weren't anything to do with me, not physically. All that remained was to be a strict materialist, and you absolutely didn't mind that your mother killed herself, I said, having strayed into sarcasm somehow. And we wound down into an uneasy sadness, the reason we didn't talk about these things. Then Will was about to go. We could feel him being about to.

At last he said, 'My pony was lovely. His name was Muffin. He used to eat my hair.' He mimicked a pony craning its muzzle round to nip at someone's hair.

'Your parents wouldn't eat your hair,' I said.

'Well, now you're just being sensible.'

'Well.' I reached up a handful of coins.

'Sprawling,' Will said, his word for *brilliant*. And left, and left his grin suspended, losing its substance, in the air; a Cheshire laughterness that made the room boo-hoo lonely. I knelt missing Seth or someone I didn't know yet, comparing my feelings to being in love, getting antsy that way, when your consciousness inhabits someone else, or dogs their footsteps around an imagined city. For a kneeling spell of shut eyes, it was the city of childhood: a crayon sketch in which Seth was the only other person in the world. Parents were tangible as a brooding fear behind my back, four parents.

Then I sighed like a serious child and got up to go tell Amos we were going to California.

4

The Brother Figure

Dreamscape, in crayon

My first memories date from when I was five, the year we lived in Florida. The memories are an unreliable, smeared phantasmagoria. Sheldon was working for a weapons manufacturer, Martin-Marietta; in my mind, apart from him, it was staffed by marionettes. I remember standing on the shore of a lake with H. R. Pufnstuf, while a brass band played jazz on the opposite shore. I remember seeing the sun grow precipitously in the sky, coming in to incinerate earth. The roads around Orlando ran through orange groves and fields of snakes. The Spanish mosses that hung from the throats of trees were the souls of bearded conquistadors.

I remember a dusty playground, empty and silent, because there are no other people left in the world. The dome-shaped jungle gym is olive-green and dull, a cage in which nothing lives. Likewise I remember a marshy field, a two-car garage, and a garden, with the people erased. Every setting from my childhood has the option of being remembered in this post-nuclear past tense.

In the playground's other, populated, past, an anxious scene is taking place. I and a band of other children circle the jungle gym cautiously, poking our heads through the bars to see. Half-buried in the sugar-dry dirt is a black widow spider. It budges in a solid mass and flips, its dead legs frozen in their empty hug. Reassured, we use the stick to cut the spider into quarters, so it can't come back to life.

Another scene: a few spiders, large and small, dot a clapboard wall. My mother is teaching me to fear them. She points at each in turn, explaining something. The world behind our backs is green and volatile, every leaf so alive it could spontaneously birth new spiders. I'm afraid of spiders for the next ten years.

At the edge of our lawn, the jungle begins. It sings and shrieks and smells. I make a rushing crashing as I push through the foliage, which is dense and sticky with wet. At the jungle's edge, I break out into a realm of blossoming orchards and white stone roads.

It's a kingdom. Along the roads, sultans ride painted elephants. The howdahs and the sultans are simple drawings, but their mounts are dusty, sweating, real beasts. In the ivory palace lives a princess whose Grand Vizier is a Siamese cat. She threads her rings, one by one, on the cat's tail for safekeeping.

These are the grounds of a bedtime story: 'How the Siamese Cat Got the Kink in Its Tail'. Somehow, over the years, they have drifted from the storybook out into the suburbs of real Orlando.

The only other thing I remember is that Seth and I were exiled all day long, every day, to this green outside that sang with insects. My mother put us out every morning when my father left. Then she kept the doors locked until an hour before my father got home.

But the point

Or perhaps it was only once, or maybe it was a dream. I may have seen it in a TV movie. It may be some other child's memory, told to me in confidence, remembered too well.

But Seth protected me. He was my most akin, my imaginary friend. And Seth wasn't frightened of spiders; Mom hadn't taught him because he was a boy. We played, immune to fear, among the rattlesnakes and the beard-souls of the Spanish conquistadors. He knew a house where they had a tyre swing; when I was with him, I wasn't scared of the people whose swing it was, who could arrest us for stealing. We swung in it playing Zorro, carving Zs in the dirt with a stick and shouting challenges to the bad rich people.

I would knock on his bedroom wall at night. He'd knock back twice for danger, three times for 'coast clear'. I'd stalk to his room in pyjamas and we'd whisper, we'd make shadow rabbits and birds with a flashlight Seth had stashed. He taught me his soundless spy walk, leading the way downstairs to the middle of the night.

I remember a time we were the only two people in the world, forever Hansel and Gretel. My brother taught me to read when I was three. Taught me to tie my shoelaces. It was my brother who was there, not my parents who were fuzzy ideas, who floated above eye level, only people in shape.

He's all that's left. Those parents are gone, replaced, rescinded. If I have a sacred, a taboo person, who was there before I knew what I was, it must be Seth.

The towering inferno

The period in which Mom killed herself, four years of it; disaster movies were in vogue, parents got divorced, the human race was about to be exterminated in a thermonuclear war.

The rot began with the Watergate trials, an evil obscure to me at eight – connected to floods, burst dams, *The Poseidon Adventure*. The ship's ballroom is upside down and Nixon's cabinet are trying to escape; room after room floods. Something about it means America will never be the same.

Watergate led directly to Louise's death. There is no need to prove a strictly causal relationship. Also, my fantasy in which I had a best friend brother didn't last into the Watergate era. These changes are the necessary steps of an algorithm, or the stages of a disease.

How I remember the decisive fight is, my brother snatched my teddy bear and threatened to burn it. We were in the soft hallway upstairs. That windowless hallway had a deep beige carpet, beige wallpaper, nothing else. The teddy bear's name was Peter, he had black beady glass eyes. I was eight and my brother was ten.

A nightlight had been plugged into the hallway outlet. It had a simpering bee painted on its hood. My brother held the teddy bear against this nightlight, saying he was going to catch fire. My heart cried out for the anguished bear, I squalled. At last Seth threw the teddy bear at me hard, with hatred or self-disgust.

A blonde little boy with hazel eyes, cherub lips. In early photos Seth looks uncertain and angry. Buck-toothed, then wears braces. The eyes photograph devil red. He always looks as if he's just lost his balance. Seth stands in the photo askew in a floppy tiger suit, a little league uniform, in plaid pants and a stripy tie, his hell eyes gleaming.

I never forgave him. I'd seen through Seth and we had no relationship for twenty-two years.

For the first few years, I refused to use a fork, or to sit on a chair, if Seth had touched them first. I wouldn't ask Seth a question. I would focus my hate on him like someone focusing the rays of the sun on an ant through a magnifying glass. Nothing happened, mysteriously Seth kept eating his macaroni and cheese, unmoved, not bothering to hate me back.

I tried to brain Seth with the metal footstool, after he chased me with the steak knife, after I whipped him with the jump-rope, after he kicked me off the love seat. I promised to put Seth's eyes out in his sleep, at the top of my lungs. He promised to kill me now, then we both stalked away, the whole world booming in our ears, *unfair, unfair.*

All things in the world were aligned with either myself or Seth; a yin/yang system. I was vanilla, blue, animals, and goodness; Seth was chocolate, red, human beings, and evil. Because my brother took French in junior high school, I took Spanish. And I scorned Seth things with the pubescent-girl ferocity that generates poltergeists. Drugs and rock'n'roll were Seth things, too – he got there two years earlier. I took sex.

In the early, happy, years, our parents made a fuss that Seth and Sheldon both had hazel eyes, my mother and I had brown eyes. She and I were left-handed, much was made of that. 'You were always Louise's favourite, so I favoured Seth,' my father told me many years later. I was Louise's child and Seth was Sheldon's, maybe that's where the line was drawn.

At a certain point, my hatred of my brother turned into fear. My mother died again and again. I began to be bullied at school by Seth's friends. In the long weeks my father was away on business, and Mom was in the hospital, Seth had chaotic parties, attended by people who bullied me at school. I hid in my room and read. It was *The Black Stallion,* then it was *Gone With the Wind,* then suddenly it was Faulkner. I read *Lolita* three times at Lolita's age, when sex and poetry were two facets of the same futile longing. Tennessee Williams taught me what love was, while cock rock and drunken voices penned me in my room. I would be waiting and waiting to sneak to the bathroom.

Seth was twelve, thirteen, fourteen. He became the archetypal grunge kid in a lumberjack shirt. Seth wore a ski hat year round, and played in a band that never played anywhere but our basement. He owned a man-sized stuffed Sylvester the cat, which was a fuck-you mascot, there to have a bong taped to its paw, to be dressed as Cheech. By then, I didn't know who he was. We hadn't spoken in years. I took life too seriously; I was all about Dostoevsky long before I understood Dostoevsky. Fun was good enough for Seth, to have twenty dollars and have good friends was good enough.

If we passed in the hallway, both of our faces would blur, we would strain to not see. In the moment when we turned sideways to pass in the narrow space, we each shrank back in petrified loathing, as if we were passing a cockroach that height.

In the other rooms, our mother died and died again and died, until she didn't return. She had scrubbed off her last trace. Our father came back instead, new-minted as a spokesman sent by Dead Louise, and seemed soaked in his tears, beet red and out of his depth like a hungry child.

Our family was over. Seth and I relaxed into not even knowing each other. We became mutually exclusive; only one of us could be at a time. It was necessary, it was our pact. We were the only two people in the world. If we met, it would break the spell that prevented our family from really having happened to us.

Times I remember Seth speaking to me

1976

The hospital where Mom lives this year is an elegant Colonial house, with braided rugs on hardwood floors, and paintings on the walls of anonymous worthies in nineteenth-century dress. There are armchairs with velvet upholstery; there are ceramic spaniels on the mantelpiece. The piano has a shawl spread over it. An orange cat pads up the stairs. The hospital has been disguised, meticulously, as someone's delightful home.

In the psychologist's office, we sit in low fat armchairs, arrayed in front of his desk. He is a spare, bearded man in a blazer and thick eyeglasses. I spend most of the session studying the spines of his books: *Fear of Freedom*; *Beyond the Pleasure Principle*; *I'm OK, You're OK*. In front of me at eye level on the desk is a snowfall paperweight I idly covet. If the psychologist asks me a question, I sit with all my muscles tensed, fiercely silent, until he gives up. Although we've never discussed it, Seth and I have the same opinion of family counselling: we're being punished for something *Mom did*.

The psychologist is saying to me, 'Your father tells me you like animals better than people.'

I stare, speechless with malice. Nothing occurs to me, clouds bound in my head. *Of course* I like animals better than people. Animals are better than people.

Gently, he suggests, 'Sometimes people can make us hurt. A lot of people find it's safer to have feelings about animals.'

I say hatefully, 'That's not the reason.'

He smiles, knowing better. Tears of fury start to my eyes. The psychologist turns to Seth and is about to speak. Seth shoots out of his chair.

Seth makes it to the door before anyone can stop him, and he's gone. The adults are up from their seats, all shouting. Down the stairs out the front door into the simple empty night of suburbia; a parking lot with crabgrass around the edges, streetlights spaced along a two-lane highway. The smell of fireplace smoke drifts through the smell of truck exhaust and by the time we're all outside, Seth's sprinting, doing his perfect touchdown run to the road. The adults spread out after him like hounds.

My brother is a miniature figure who makes no progress on the car-sized road. It looks like he's running in quicksand from where I run too. He runs as if he'll never make it. The adults book it like kids, fast as they can in earnest, shouting in earnest. Even my father's running. My mother is running, her pained voice making its perennial point, this hurts her. The psychologist is running farthest, best, in professional can-do mode, and I'm running at an angle to everyone else. If Seth escapes I'll go too. Seth can't get away with this, I deserve to run away more. And there's something about him running that makes you realise, as if you woke up from a dream to find the house had filled with smoke, there is no time to waste. Run for your life.

But suddenly, making me sick and faltering, Seth falters. Seth slows down; from where I'm running, slowing in twinned motion, there's no call. The whole world shows its other, pitiless, face, where no one ever escapes. You have to go to school in the morning. You'll be back when you're hungry.

The adults circle him. Seth says nothing for all they needle him. Finally, he breaks away and walks back to the hospital a little ahead of them, head ducked. I catch up to him and we go in together, rushing to vehemently separate ourselves from the adults. As he goes up the stairs, Seth says over his shoulder, casually, softly, 'It's OK, Sandy.'

We haven't spoken for years. It's like a god speaking through him.

Dad never makes us go back to family counselling again.

1978

Dad comes home sobbing and red, wet all over; my mother has been found dead in her car. At length, I rise from the opiate gold plush sofa and go to the kitchen, where the lights have all been turned off except for the stove light. Dad has gone up to talk to Seth. I find a can of Tab and the Pringles potato chips. I walk upstairs as if I'm mounting the air to the purple drifting clouds of evening, and the stairs are dark and close.

Upstairs, I go into my parents' room, eating Pringles potato chips. No one's there; I close the door behind me. I'm slotting my hand in the potato chip cylinder and teasing out moulded stacks of chips. I half-sit on the edge of my parents' king-sized bed, on the stiff comforting ridges of wire in the electric blanket, and eat potato chips, one frail chip saddling my tongue at a time. I eat with the repetitive motions of assembly-line machinery.

On the chestnut bureau across from me is a rubber figurine of Oliver Hardy. It has a wind-up key; wound, the figurine should waddle in the manner of Oliver Hardy. Now the mechanism is worn out. Hardy will only budge in place, as if being shoved again and again. The figure represents my father as all fat sidekicks do.

Oliver Hardy looks into the air, jolly, rocked back on one heel. Ten minutes pass.

Seth flings open the door with a crash like breaking the door down, shouting, 'What the fuck! Dad's been looking for you for an hour!'

I shoot to my feet. Pringles scatter over the floor. I'm immediately crying and gasping for breath.

'What the fuck's the matter with you?' Seth grimaces at the chips on the floor. 'Clean that up, you idiot.'

I stand hunched, weeping with the cylinder in my hand. I can't move as long as Seth's looking at me. I can't speak.

Seth says, 'I'll give you something to cry about.'

But once upon a time, for the last time (I am ever saying this) we were a family: we were in love

and every summer, we drove to Florida, Cocoa Beach, and stayed at beach motels with names like 'Marco Polo', 'Thunderbird', 'Kismet'. We'd stop at roadside firework stands to buy our neighbourhood's Fourth of July bottle rockets, illegal in Mass. We were smugglers, outlaws, Seth and I in ecstasy. Every year we stopped for the night at Rocky Mount, North Carolina, a town of all hotels that was a wonderland, the stand of towering neon signs as fantastical as Santa's village. You could race on the Ramada's concrete balconies, bare feet smacking the smooth cold surface, to the soda machine. The alien Carolina swampy woods had a scent of lustrous mud. A restaurant there once served me a perfect vanilla tart I never found again; it became a magical entity for me like a faun.

At some point I always got hysterical because Seth's elbow tip had crossed over onto my side of the seat. 'Mom, he's going to *touch* me.'

At some point we played 'washing machine', the soles of our bare feet pressed together, pedalling in tandem. The fact that Seth condescended to touch me made me fall and fall inside with joy.

I lay on my back and watched the crowns of trees pass upside down. The telephone wires were scored on trembling blue; the sun slipped from branch to branch, flaring and folding its wings. If I squinted the right way, I would see the other world where wolves and trees could talk. I was falling asleep and going there, with my eyes shut I rode the songs on the radio; 'Killing Me Softly', 'Crocodile Rock', songs oceanic and shimmering with unfathomable adult significance.

The motel nights where headlights fled across the ceiling; blasting the day's sandcastle with firecrackers; Dad points at the ocean's muzzy horizon and says, 'That's France.' It's the world in which it's OK to be a child, in someone's power like a toy. All happy families are alike.

When my father announced he was divorcing my mother, she said she would move to Florida. She said it defiantly gladly, hinting she still had tricks up her sleeve. She said she had always been happy there; then she lost momentum, and talked about her future ineffectually, the way a person may feebly perform an unwelcome task, to goad someone else into taking the tools from her hands.

And she killed herself ineffectually, in public, using the same prescription she had OD'd on many times without success. She died, it just so happened. My father came home sobbing with the news. He told me, then he went upstairs to tell my brother.

What my father told me about that scene:

Seth sat stiff through the news, face blank. He hadn't turned off the television. It was *Candlepins for Cash* or something like that, nothing.

At last my father said – gently like gently prising loose the stubborn cap of a jar with a butterknife blade so the vacuum seal breaks, air sucks in, and the cap will twist off easy – my father said, 'Are you thinking we're better off without her?'

My brother began to cry. My father, crying, said, 'Because I think that, too. It's not your fault, Seth. That's just the way it is.'

*   *   *

And I run along Cocoa Beach at midnight, I'm barefoot in the sand and the wandering shallows. I'm thirty-eight, and visiting another, better mother. A 'real', 'blood', mother, not a government mother. I run a loping hour alongside the coursing reflection of stars and moonlight, while my mother, Sally Greenawalt, is working late. She's in Florida on a business trip for NASA. At this moment, she's listening in on an uplink to the astronauts on the shuttle from the base at Cape Canaveral.

I run past the Marco Polo, its rows of pastel doors, and I try to believe this is the Cocoa Beach Louise was in, where moonlight foundered in the chlorinated pool, the hotel bedspreads smelled of mothballs. I try to believe she existed once, for a while padding up the beach I try. Then I'm in the shower at Sally's motel, elated from salt spray in my lungs, salt/sweat film on my skin. My heart lopes like to last for ever. In love with myself as my new mother's child, I lie on the fold-out sighing with physical bliss, picking up Sally's airplane book, *White Teeth*.

So I was better off without Louise, unequivocally. We were all better off. The world was a happier place; no one lost out. But Louise never got the chance to run barefoot down a moonlit beach, sentimental about a new mother, as if bad Ida had been recalled by the manufacturer, as if good daughters went to heaven, as if it wasn't just *as if* (for a moment on the beach with your sun-flickering eyes devoutly shut) but your mother came true.

5

The Adult Frog Box

It's because you were given up for adoption. It's because your mother killed herself when you were thirteen. That made you anxious, unstable, hypersensitive. As an adult, you didn't know how to trust. Critical of everything, you fumed at the vapid conversation at the next table, Labour's tax policy, Kierkegaard's dumb ideas. Everybody understands this logical progression; your unhappy childhood made you an unhappy adult.

You don't believe that cant. Trauma isn't personality. You are the product of countless experiences, insights, forays of free will. You fashioned yourself, at the prompting of a mystery. Kierkegaard's works are objectively dumb. You never even think about the 'unhappy childhood'. Whatever you are, however pathological, is what you decided to be.

Then you meet your biological parents. And they are exactly like you.

I get off the Greyhound bus in San Jose

with Amos straggling behind. My task is to find my mother, of whom I have never seen even a photo, among the strangers in the Greyhound station at San Jose. As she will always be, she's lagging a little behind everyone. The people thin, departing for their parked cars, and Sally still gives the impression of being jostled and pushed around when there are only two or three people left.

We don't have a striking physical resemblance. In ways, I look more like Louise. Sally isn't Jewish; I look Jewish. Sally has a waspy pixieish prettiness, ideal in a librarian, a bit Kate Hepburn. I have Sally's body, not her face.

She's a woman about the right age, looking for someone. Since I fit the profile, she keeps looking at me. In stages, she becomes my mother, smiling more as she walks up.

She says, 'Well – hi!' in surprise and gratification, meaning it's amazing we pulled this off. She says, 'Sandy!'

Then she baulks, aware that there's an etiquette she missed, there are right things her sisters would have known to say. She blurts out, 'I should introduce myself. Oh no, I'm so bad at this.'

'You're not,' I blurt, and sound so like her I feel exposed.

Amos says cordially, 'I'm the sham husband. Hi.' He extends his hand.

Sally blinks as if sun-blinded, shaking Amos's hand while looking at me. At last, she says, 'This is just so incredible! Welcome!'

Sally the Good, in whom I once lived for nine months

was right away my favourite person. Sally had my opinions and I had her fumbling mannerisms. Her need to introspect while the practical things of life crashed down around her ears was mine; it was futile giving directions, care instructions, or houseplants to either of us. Space science (one example) was a breeze, but you couldn't trust us to make toast first try. Boyfriends did the cooking; friends rebuttoned our shirts and turned our collars down. I found this galling in myself, but any wrong thing she did was sweet, I liked her so damned much. I liked myself much better once she was my mother.

Sally muttered under her breath, or blurted in a voice that subtly cracked. Her manner was self-effacing, but what she said was candid fearlessly. That her mother hated her. That Republicans all had weird upbringings, and it made them come out mean. She was the girl who threw bricks into shop windows to protest against the Vietnam War, and the girl who apologised after everything she said, who felt uncomfortable in bright colours.

Her house was a shack in the redwood forest of the Santa Cruz mountains, where shacky homes are pasted high and low like mushrooms to the slopes. The roads are widened animal trails; curling, criss-crossed dirt tracks that make it impossible to order pizza in these parts. The occasional day-glo yellow banana slug can be seen two hills away, paused on a patch of quartzy sand.

Once when I visited in later years, the house was being repaired, and a wall of the living room where I slept was gone. Waking up, I looked straight off a slope into the shifting upper crowns of redwoods. The house was always treehouse-like, even with all four walls. Indoors, it had outdoors air. The background noise to conversation was crickets, birdsong, flurries of wind in branches. There was a spectral, chilly scent of sap.

Nothing in the house was built to code or common sense. Hot was cold; cold was hot. The furniture was comfortable, beige, the default pieces people get if they don't shop. A red flannel sheet had been nailed over the entrance to the living room in lieu of a door. The wood-burning stove in winter was a real hearth which ate time while you fiddled kindling into place and nudged logs into flame, a hearth over which you fussed, tending to the fire that was demanding as an infant. Like an infant also it shed meaning, the smoky fire your racial memory craved made you feel whole.

In the mornings on the deck, where light pricked through the redwood fronds and the air soared with you as the boughs fled over the light and bounced, jays flew above you and below. A dog on a neighbouring deck downhill would bark the same three-note tune over and over, as if he was meditating. Sitting there with a book was a serenity so exact it made me restless. I would keep getting up to fetch something, trying to refine it, *do* it, because being in her house felt too intense to be a passive experience.

I'd had a letter from her before I came. In four handwritten pages, she'd told me about her Berkeley radical years, her job at NASA, and 'the work I still do on myself', a therapy-speak wrong note to me, it came off mawkish. I didn't tell anyone about that part. But this was Northern California: all the people Sally knew were New Age pagans who discussed their gurus with their therapists chosen by their psychics (who were married to programmers who paid all the bills). Irreducibly, the people were plainfolks Midwest, nevertheless. I could never afterwards separate paganism from the novelty cat mug; the two never seemed to occur in isolation.

Sally was a failure (to many of her female peers) because she had no children. Her marriage had flickered out, leaving her becalmed alone at forty-two. Her married sisters with their broods pitied her from the depths of their hearts, tiptoed around the tender subject until it perforce got tender to her, too. And she got forlorn, for instance, about her messy house. If she could have picked a skill to master: cooking. When she learned to dress respectably, in her fifties, she was infatuated with her new wardrobe, bought in a whirlwind breakthrough week. Then she forgot to do it again: or there was never time, between her work, the scuba-diving trips to Central America, new boyfriends, the men she cheated on them with – all things that didn't count when women had them. At least to her married friends, the story was: poor Sally has no family.

Amos flew back to London the night after we arrived. With him dispensed with, Sally took me to meet everyone she knew. The car became the default setting; a scope of exhaust-hazed highways and yellow mountains, a window breeze with the sweet, papery texture of bakery air; me talking about my life, Sally talking about her life. She gave me a tour of her: to fully know Sally, I must know Chris and Carrie and Sally's new friend KZ who had recently married herself in a public ceremony. I had to go to her therapy group and have a shiatsu session with her practitioner. The oldest friend was Marta, a solid, garrulous woman with the cosy presence of a talking, matron-sized animal from a children's film. Mrs Badger in mom jeans and a pretty blouse put on to meet me, Marta was made maudlin, unstitched, by my materialisation – Sally hadn't told anyone I existed before. When we went to breakfast at Marta's house, she'd bought forty scones and muffins, that potlatch quantity representing the flood of her feelings.

The day Sally took me to the NASA offices, we nipped into the lab where she'd started out years before as a tech, and met her old friend Mel. He, a soft-spoken black guy who gave me the grand tour equably, also paused from time to time to squint at Sally, going, 'I'll show your *daughter* . . . where it all happened,' or, 'It's sure nice to meet . . . *your daughter*,' because she'd told him years before she didn't have any kids.

'Oh, I'll explain to him later,' she said, offhand, leading me out past a Godzilla-scale wind tunnel. 'Those are new aircraft. Prototypes or something. I don't know what anything is. Hi, Mary – this is my daughter!'

From being a lab technician at NASA, Sally had become a crew trainer, teaching the astronauts to carry out experiments on the space shuttle. She was liaison between the scientists and the astronauts, who were in the main ex Air Force, action hero types. The crews hatched quails in space, raised microgravity corn that grew in mazy curls, bred weightless tadpoles. Everything was skewed or sideways; everything needed earth to thrive. The astronauts themselves lost bone mass, lost so much in muscle mass their hearts were feeble. After longer times in space, they were carried from the shuttle on stretchers. Then they'd start, as soon as they were up and about, to agitate for another flight.

It wasn't for the trip itself, the transformational sight of gem-like earth in the space shuttle window, not primarily. It was the kudos. NASA life was ruled and made coherent by the gravitational pull of status. Even Sally felt a leaden depression when she was later promoted out of the spotlight. The office politics were so fierce they took on a *Lord of the Flies* aspect. As soon as you were assigned to a project, someone began to scheme to steal it. Half the work was getting your name on things, and the other half was removing other people's. In your spare time, you got colleagues into trouble. Sally's main role in the fray was to whine about it to her boyfriend Willy. Sally didn't have a Machiavellian side. He, a NASA stalwart, used to impatiently tell her to play the game; there was no point complaining that rugby wasn't checkers, just learn the rules. And you couldn't fault his logic, although in time it grew clear believing this made him an asshole.

One woman became Sally's special nemesis. Everything Sally did was interpreted as infringement of her rights, and turned into the subject of indignant memos and secret meetings. In the midst of this, one day Sally found herself walking down a long corridor with this woman approaching from the opposite end. The nemesis studiously glared at the wall. A full minute passed as the two walked towards each other, heels clicking in the otherwise silent hallway. The nemesis kept her eyes stonily averted. As they finally passed each other, Sally found herself muttering, 'Crybaby!' The woman lodged a complaint about the crybaby incident the following day.

Equally trying was the bureaucracy. All employees received a book explaining the acronyms used at NASA, a dictionary-sized tome with tens of thousands of entries. Every year employees were required to attend a fire safety demonstration ('This is a fire extinguisher. Pass it around.') even if they were literally rocket scientists. Once the NASA engineers wanted to include a screwdriver in the payload for use in unscrewing the front panel of something called the 'Adult Frog Box'. A memo was sent asking them to design this piece of equipment. They replied that there was no need to design a screwdriver, since screwdrivers had existed for thousands of years; as long as screws. All they received was a reminder that specs had to be provided for all hardware. That process got so maddening, with the engineers repeatedly sending notes saying, 'We just want to fly a *screwdriver*,' and the higher-ups insisting on specifications, that finally the engineers scratched the screwdriver from the plans and Scotch-taped a dime to the bottom of the Adult Frog Box before the flight.

On the other hand: Sally got to know the astronauts and later the cosmonauts. She listened in on the uplink to the shuttle from Houston and from Cape Canaveral. Photos of Sally exist in which she floats in mid-air in a fighter plane which is flying parabolas to mimic conditions of microgravity. Her weightless comrades drift around her. An astronaut holds a frog in one hand, trying to induce egg-laying in weightlessness. Everyone is laughing so hard their eyes are visibly wet.

'Oh, I know, it's a wonderful thing,' she'll say. 'I guess it's so long since I cared about space science. All right, it's pretty wonderful. But!' And she'll frown stubbornly at the highway, taking another turn with her jaw set in insistence that 'wonderful' was really a word *they'd* use, and *they* weren't even truthful.

So, there was meeting friends, seeing NASA, and watching her bicker with Willy at night, but mostly stories digressing into other stories that dovetailed with new stories that fleshed out previous stories, while the little Toyota swooped down valleys and the papery breeze blew saltier, heavier, as we approached the coast. Sally told me about her sisters and her embattled teen years. She told me she'd believed I would be better off being raised by someone conventional. If I was anything like her, I would need a guide to the world. 'I never felt like I knew how to live. I thought pretty much anybody would be more useful,' Sally said, and gave me a sidelong grimace. 'Sorry.'

She came from a Midwest middle-class family fallen on hard times. She had three sisters, including one fraternal twin, outgoing Susan. Susan stood in Sally's light her whole youth long. She was a cheerleader, popular as that implies, while Sally was silent, complicated, the black sheep who climbed out of her bedroom window nights to meet unscrupulous boys. Mom was always on Sally's case, everything Sally thought was bad and was to be sanitised, suppressed.

Dad (an engineer) had had heart problems, then got Parkinson's and became a querulous armchair presence. He became 'Don't bother Daddy', and lingeringly died in the one quiet room of a house of girls. And there are more stories to him than fit here: how Dad fought in both world wars, was part of the D-Day Landing, tried to write a memoir once; all the stories that were closed behind the glum, withdrawn, prematurely old man Sally knew.

Sally was the smart one – Stanford on a scholarship. She was good at languages, ending up with Russian arbitrarily, drifting into things like teens do. She got As because poor girls had to. Her college job was in the library; and there would never be a time that Sally didn't work, or when she liked her job.

Otherwise, she was wild. That meant she slept with boys but also meant the wayward inward streak that made her a Berkeley radical. She'd started that as a rank-and-file protester, then got a job copy-editing *Ramparts*, the main organ of the Left. In the *Ramparts* office, Sally met everybody in the Free Speech Movement, SDS, the Black Panthers. Later famous and infamous radicals lounged around that office quibbling over points of ideology, emoting about their casualties, and bragging about exploits against the pigs. The mix of drugs and common danger gave those years the sloppy, indiscriminate intimacy of the 4 a.m. dregs of a party. Sally knows stray secrets about Tom Hayden, Huey P. Newton et al., though she was the lowly copy-editor, after all, those big shots weren't her intimate friends.

She and her husband Robbie went to consciousness-raising groups and belonged to a 'food conspiracy'. Because she'd taken marksmanship as her sports requirement in school, Sally ran a class teaching women to use firearms so they could fight in the revolution. She and Robbie used to stockpile guns in their apartment. Once they were robbed and all the guns were taken. Then they had to go over every inch of floor with a vacuum cleaner, then with sponges, then with paper towels, making sure no trace of marijuana was left before they called the cops.

'Everyone had these communes, but we had no idea how to treat each other. There were always fights about cleaning. I mean – there were two women's communes, and one of them made a complaint about the other one, saying it was elitist. And it really was! All the popular people were in that commune. God. We wanted to make a new society, but we couldn't even get along with each other. We were just so young.

'It's hard to remember now what it was like. People were *dying* over there. We were knocking on doors every day and trying so hard to come up with arguments. I don't think I changed one single person's mind. But we were right! We had all the facts, we could prove we were right. But nobody wanted to listen, so they just didn't. It made you crazy after a while.

'We were always high then. We smoked grass from the time we woke up. I don't know how we could have gotten through all that if we weren't on drugs.

Long before the war was over, it stopped being just about the war. The people were rising in Washington, Chicago, in the capitals of Europe. A new, more rational order would raise all people above brute needs and the piddling greeds that drove American capitalism. Mankind would be transfigured; wise and whole.

'At the end, bad things seemed to happen to people who wouldn't give up. A lot of people got hurt, or died, and you started to think maybe somebody was really getting rid of them. The FBI put in provocateurs who would try to get people to do more violent things, more extreme things. We all got so paranoid. But we were right to be paranoid. The government was spying on us! And we were stoned all the time! How could you not be paranoid?' (Sally huffed a breath out, shaking her pixieish head, and reached to downshift as we approached a hill. The sun held steady, bearing the dun scene forward bravely in its stiff bright palm. Sally took another breath and went on.)

The sixties are often said to have 'ended' at Altamont, a music festival where Hell's Angels hired to provide security attacked an unruly audience: in the course of the night, four people were killed. For Sally and Robbie, the sixties ended at the Sky River Valley Festival in Washington state. No one died at that festival. Nothing of historic importance happened. Sally and Robbie watched the acts, talked to people and smoked pot without incident. On the way home, nevertheless, they were so stricken neither of them spoke for the three-hour drive.

For the first time in years, they'd met young people who weren't a part of the radical scene. None of these American kids were political. None of them were preparing for the revolution the Berkeley protesters expected imminently, which they believed the working classes were arming for. That was never going to happen. The Vietnam War was over, and the revolution was a sterile fantasy.

'Well, it was crushing. We'd had no idea. We really thought the revolution was about to happen, and everything would be OK. Robbie had given up his PhD. He just never finished his math dissertation. I think we were depressed for years after that . . . I'm still depressed!'

'I missed all that,' Marta interjected sourly (at this point in the story we'd stopped by Marta's place for tea; we were finishing off the potlatch scones from two days previous). 'I was just married. I was busy getting married, having kids, and then getting divorced.'

'Well, I was married, too,' Sally muttered. 'Technically. Technically I have a kid.' She looked at me, and said, 'You!' We both laughed; my being Sally's child was still like a trick we were playing. I was the rabbit out of the hat.

Marta forged on, oblivious. 'All those marriages that ended in divorce, yeesh. The men all dumped their wives at forty, and found a woman ten years younger. That was our generation.'

'It's true,' said Sally, deciding to play ball. 'And the second wife would look a lot like the first wife when she was the same age. It was amazing, they really did do that. Robbie did that.'

'A-holes,' Marta said.

'Though I cheated on Robbie first,' Sally suddenly remembered. 'Technically. I was kind of going with Tony. Oh, well.'

I said, 'How did you get into NASA from working at *Ramparts*?'

'Oh, that.' Sally made a face. 'Robbie and I had decided to do something useful to society, since the revolution wasn't coming. We were going to be auto-mechanics, but that was so ridiculous.' All of us started to giggle. Sally said, laughing helplessly, 'It's true! So we studied to be medical technologists.'

Marta shook her head at me ruefully. 'Wow. Your mother was a dummy!'

'That was how I met Marta,' Sally said. 'She's still doing it.'

'It's a stinky profession.' Marta counted on her fingers: 'It's four years of school, it's badly paid, it's dull, you're in a lab all day in ugly fluorescent lighting, you're using toxic chemicals . . . what did I miss?'

'Well, my first job was in a paediatric cancer ward. Every morning I had to take blood from children who were dying. God, it was so miserable. I used to take Valium every morning to be able to face it. When I got home, all I wanted to do was whine. That really finished me and Robbie. Well, that and the affair.'

Then Sally's attention slipped to Marta, who'd been gazing at me in the meanwhile, tears beginning to well. 'Oh, no,' Sally said.

Marta suddenly stood up, wailing, 'I can't help it! It's so wonderful, this is amazing. Here you are! Sally's daughter! I hope you know Sally always missed you.'

Sally muttered, 'Well. Not really.'

I laughed. Marta said, 'You did! You told me so!' outraged.

'Oh, all right. Have it your way,' Sally said. And to me, in an undertone, 'Not really.'

I said, 'Good. I mean, I don't want you to have missed—'

'But here you are!' said Marta bossily. 'Somebody have another muffin and just ignore me. The pumpkin ones are yummy.'

Back in the car, Sally said, 'Well, it made you want to say, "It's not *that* wonderful."' She started the car and said, 'OK, I missed you. But the way she made it sound! Blech!'

Missing an infant

I was born in the middle of a blackout of the Eastern Seaboard. The region from Ontario to Connecticut lost its electricity while Sally gave birth to me: a baby of ordinary weight, length, health. Her telegram to Susan: *Little girl born stop dark curly hair stop funny-looking baby stop.* She nursed me for seven days before I was taken away. By then she hadn't seen my real father in months; they wouldn't see each other for twenty-six years.

I don't know why my parents were ever together when by all accounts they made each other miserable. They shared four months of miscommunication punctuated by sex, a dispiriting waste neither party would remember clearly. But youth is like two bottles of wine; things done under its influence aren't you. Youth's tribulations spring from humours or miasmas, from fantastic things that never were. Dawn should wash them off, years should.

But she got pregnant. She and my father were already breaking up when they found out.

Abortion was against the law then. Sally might have gone to Mexico, but weeks passed and she just hadn't. Months passed and she decided she didn't believe in abortion anyway. And Sally knew she couldn't be a single mother: she wasn't heroic or devil-may-care enough. Girls in 1965 didn't raise kids alone, middle-class girls didn't. On the other hand, she liked me – biologically, pre-rationally. She was one of those women for whom pregnancy is a duplicated health, a rosy, heavy sufficiency. She put off making the decision to give me up for the longest time.

The only member of her family who knew about me was

her twin sister, Susan. Susan had to be told: before Sally ever met my father, she and Susan had planned to take a trip through Europe after graduation. Sally would now be travelling five months' pregnant. A few weeks before the scheduled trip, in the first of many dramatic flip-flops, Sally borrowed money from Susan to get an abortion. At the airport, Sally admitted the baby was still there, though the money was gone.

(Sally: 'Oh, no. I forgot all about that!'

Susan: 'I didn't forget.')

The trip went on as planned. They stayed in cheap hotels and saw the commonly prescribed sights through France, Germany, Spain. Then in Barcelona Sally met an Israeli single mother. This lady (name lost in mists) advised her to raise her child in Israel. The state would support her. To Israelis, illegitimacy bore no stigma. Not telling anyone, Sally went to Greece and booked passage on a boat to Haifa. That absorbed her last cash, and in Piraeus she was cared for by a benevolent shoeshine boy for the few days before the ship sailed. She disembarked in Haifa broke. Assorted charitable strangers took her in. On a stranger's couch one night, again she changed her plan. She would give me up for adoption in Tel Aviv, to settle me outside the Christian faith. 'I just thought the whole story of Christianity was debilitating, especially to women. But to anyone! That crucifixion . . . it was *not* a nice story.'

But at the adoption agency in the morning, they told her both parents must be Jewish for me to be given to a Jewish home.

'Well, they are,' Sally tried. 'We are.'

Producing documents to that effect was beyond her power, though, since she was Lutheran on both sides. Stymied, and uncertain she could last another three months in Israel – she hadn't done laundry all this time – Sally gave up.

At last one of the people who'd been helping her – an Israeli policeman who'd let her sleep in his barracks one night – arranged for Sally to phone her mother long distance. Money was wired, and Sally flew home to Seattle.

(Susan: 'You left me waiting in Lisbon without a word for two weeks. I had no idea where you'd gone.'

Sally: 'Oh, God . . . Sandy, don't tell anyone about that. Oh, OK, you can tell people. Damn.')

Back in the US, Sally stayed the last few months with her old high-school friend Frank in Boston. He took her to her obstetrics appointments at the Crittenden on his Vespa, dropping her off around the corner because the Crittenden people were so strait-laced. Boyfriends weren't allowed to visit. Sally hid the fact that she smoked. Some unwed mothers went in intending to keep their children, but the Crittenden people had a policy of steering them towards adoption. A respectable married couple would be better for any baby, the prejudice was.

I was born, and this time Sally got her Jewish couple. The baby was in safe hands; she left the hospital; life went on. The new jam Sally got into effaced the old, nothing more to say. Only, Sally missed me for twenty-five years.

I missed my mother for twenty-five years. And I dreamed about her once as a brooding child in a Florida motel room drifting off to the TV news from the Middle East. My real mother was a slender, dark-haired Syrian woman, who stood forlorn at a barbed-wire fence which excluded her from the land of Israel.

6

The Worms

Sheldon used to say that when he died, his dirty movie collection would go to Harvard. The scope of that collection wasn't unusual: a few dozen videos, most of them softcore stuff recorded from cable. The feeble joke was his way of complaining that he'd been short-changed in love. A variation was, 'Hey, at least I've got my dirty movies to keep me warm,' delivered in his Groucho Marx voice.

Before the age of videos (in Louise's lifetime) it was novels. Some were pulp with black-and-white covers and names like *Truck Stop Slut* or *The Rampant Rapist*. Some were glossy Sexual-Revolution-era bestsellers: *The Happy Hooker, He, The Devil in Miss Jones*. My favourites were the Christina series (*Christina's Promise, Christina's Nights*, etc.) by Blakely St James. They told the orgiastic sexploits of lubriciously luscious heiress Christina van Bell. In the Christina-verse, no one was ever unhappy. Even when kidnapped into white slavery, sold at auction, incarcerated in a sheikh's harem, the characters consoled themselves with sexploits and sly pleasantries. It was Merchant Ivory porn, in which lush settings, banter, and champagne made even gang rape a frivolous misadventure.

Rape wasn't stigmatised in porn then. Neither was child abuse or incest. (A typical Blakely St James scene involved a request for 'incense' being misunderstood by a maniacally hospitable Arab host.) Child-themed porn was fairly common: there was an X-rated *Alice in Wonderland*, and an episodic skinflick based on nursery rhymes. My father was not inclined that way, although I did find in his sock drawer a porno comic featuring Little Orphan Annie. The O-eyed doodle was pictured being screwed by Daddy Warbucks, 69-ing other orphans, and taking it in the ass off her dog Sandy, with unfunny captions.

That comic was the first porn I remember finding disturbing. I stood at the sock drawer reading every page, too frightened to stop. It was like a bug I had to kill, whose last twitches I must stop, before I would be able to sleep. That comic book implied all inhumanity; it expressed the indigestible fact that children are raped while adults do not care. Still, the pictures made me horny.

Obscenity: it causes a swift and piercing depression. It is 'filthy' because your mind is irreversibly polluted. You know in your bones you will never be the same. Then you distract yourself and the feeling passes.

In a vase in front of me, three fake flowers Louise had made with a kit were pale with dust. (Here passes the thought that she's in the mental hospital.) I had shut the drawer, but the drawer was changed. My father was.

The videos appeared around the time of my mother's death. My father bought a special video cabinet to hold them, that stood beside his bed. I never watched them. By that time I was old enough to picture my father watching them. Their presence, in fact, made his room into a site of masturbation. Passing it at night, I felt a breeze of that unwholesome tension. I had a horror of certain washcloths I spotted in the hamper, stained in a whitish way I found suspicious. I could not have shaken my father's hand without that thought being uppermost. In practice, by that time I never touched him.

When I was fifteen, Sheldon had a heart attack. It was a minor one he first mistook for indigestion. He spent four days in the hospital under observation. He never had another heart attack again, until the day he died.

Many years later he complained that I had never visited. He said, with a resentful edge, 'That hurt my feelings, Sandy.'

I didn't contradict him then, but I remember visiting him. I remember standing by Sheldon's hospital bed, afraid of the tubes, afraid of his body that might any second kill him. He was telling me when he would come home. Really no one ever came home from the hospital. They never came home, and the hospital smell was as familiar as a baby blanket crushed to my nose. I didn't know what to say, and was repelled by my father's body in its paper robe that didn't wholly cover him, and loathed myself for thinking that when I should have been helping to save his life.

but not just; my friend Julie's father sexually abused his kids. It had happened when she was a toddler. She and her sister both confessed their memories in family counselling. 'I guess he thought we wouldn't remember,' Julie said, blasé, in the high-school smoking area, to an admiring crowd. 'Sorry, Dad.' Her mother had walked in on it once, was how she knew for sure. It was the secret reason for her parents' divorce.

The worst: her older brother could never remember or confess, because he was severely mentally retarded. Jamie couldn't talk. He wore a diaper as a teen. He also suffered from 'tactile aversion'. He didn't like anything to touch him; sometimes he became violent when compelled to put on clothes. It was due to a neurological defect, allegedly. Julie raised her eyebrows. 'May-be . . .'

Still she went to dinner with her father once a week. 'I'm sorry for him,' Julie said. 'He's really sad all the time, really.' She was a naturally, maybe preternaturally, sweet person, and at this point her teen tough gloss would fail her. She would be herself: a chubby kid in hand-me-downs, sucking a bummed cigarette and frowning, worried about her dad.

Julie's father's porn books were kept in a trailer behind her father's house. The star item was *Pre-Teen Sex Club*. As the title implies, it was a tale of horny ten-year-olds who seduced grown-ups, including their own parents. His other books were similarly extreme. In them, rape was the default form of sexual intercourse. A typical scene: the victim wets herself from fear, and the sheriff-rapist punches her unconscious for her dirty habits.

For her fourteenth birthday, Julie went to dinner with her father. On the way home he showed her a catalogue he'd received from an escort service, asking her advice about his choice. The catalogue showed the girls to the waist, in bikini tops. He was confiding about which features excited him. There were no prices listed, but Julie's father said it started out at fifty bucks. So she told me: by this time it was a private, blurted, confidence. It was something she had intended to keep secret.

Later that year, her father asked her outright if she would have sex with him. On the way home from their weekly dinner, he pulled over to the side of the road. 'Julia, I get so lonely . . . would you?' were the words he used. Then he tried to touch her breast. After she turned him down, he drove her home in a tight-lipped fury, thanks for nothing.

'If I don't see him, I have to go to court. It's in the custody arrangements. But my father doesn't have anybody else to talk to, anyway.' Julie, avoiding my eye, shrugged. 'I feel sorry for him . . .'

Confusingly, many years later, Julie recanted. The abuse never really happened, or it maybe never happened. She wasn't sure what happened. Her memory wasn't clear. She knew she'd liked the attention she got as a victim. 'In our gang, trauma equalled status, you know what they were like. It gave me power.'

So perhaps it was tall tales. That may have been Julie's weakness. When I first met her, seven years old, she told me she had a pet cheetah. It didn't live in her house; that would be cruel. It lived in Africa. Every summer her family travelled to Africa, where she would climb from the ship and call the cheetah, which would loyally speed through Africa to lick her face.

And I believed in Julie's cheetah for the same compelling reason most things are believed. I wanted it to be true. A thing as good as that (or as Marxism, or as heaven) could not be a lie; it would violate all morality.

I believed in her incestuous father for another common reason prodigies are believed. It was what frightened me most.

The personals

Sheldon placed his first ad in the local classified magazine, the *Want Advertiser,* roughly a year after Louise's death. His aim was marriage, and he didn't want some young girl, but he did need his partner to be 'attractive'. This stipulation ruled out overweight ladies and almost all women his age. He was a faithful, easy-going guy with a house and a steady job. That should be enough for most women, Sheldon never stopped believing.

At forty-eight, he was a man whose legs were coated in nacreous purple webs of varicose veins. His weight had settled and Sheldon was teardrop-shaped. He walked painfully slowly, labouring and huffing. His long-standing hernia further incapacitated him, and he was too obese to safely undergo surgery. Although Sheldon was politically liberal, he was a child of the thirties. In his mind, it would have been bizarre, verging on blameworthy, for a woman to regard these matters seriously in choosing a mate.

For thirteen years, Sheldon dated women unsuccessfully through the personal ads. On first dates, he weeded out the overweight ladies, the ones who froze at the sight of him, and the loonies. The women who made the cut might seem very charming at first. 'But after a while,' Sheldon liked to say, 'the worms come out!' He would wriggle his fingers in the air and say it in a Vincent Price voice.

There was the woman who believed in pyramid power, and the woman who talked about nothing but her last boyfriend, now in prison. The soft-hearted dog-catcher who had fourteen rescue dogs became a friend, though Sheldon always rolled his eyes about her. Others were never more than cautionary tales.

'When I got there she was drunk. Oh, boy! She was all *over* the place. She tried to kiss me, but she hadn't washed. Sandy, she actually smelled. It was gross!'

'I don't know ... she had a tumour taken out, so she couldn't have sex for six weeks. But then she had some other problem. I don't know if she's ever going to sleep with me.'

'Then she said she needed a certificate proving I don't have HIV. It's nuts! I haven't had the chance to get HIV in ... a long time.'

Two of his girlfriends died of heart attacks the same year. One was thirty-one, an anorexic felled in mid-aerobics. The other, thirty-eight, had already been diagnosed with a heart condition when she died alone in bed, a Domino's pepperoni pizza, half-eaten, on the pillow beside her. My father told me about these deaths in a tone which verged on disapproval. Coming on top of everything else, these early deaths seemed deviant. They bore out his observation that most available women were 'fruitcakes'.

A new girlfriend who was, refreshingly, his age seemed ideal until she had a few drinks. Then she told him flatly that all she wanted was to stay home all day watching television. That was what she wanted from a husband.

Spookily, his next girlfriend repeated this with the single innovation that she wanted to move to Florida first and then spend all day watching television.

'The worms come out! Brrr!'

He said, 'I'd go to a lady of the night, but I'm too scared of the diseases I'd catch. I'm chicken!'

Or, 'I think it's time for me to join the Monastery of the Merry Monks.'

Or, 'At least I've got my dirty movies to keep me warm. When I die, I'm going to leave my collection to Harvard . . .' because he was the kind of man who said the same things again and again, and who discussed his sex life with his teenaged daughter.

I'd say, 'Dad, please,' but I didn't want to spell it out. If I made (incest) explicit, our relationship would have to end. I would never be able to look him in the eye again. I would look at my tense hands, burningly silent. Ten minutes later, I'd be picking a fight over something unrelated – politics or his taste in movies, confirming his opinion that I was an 'intellectual snob'.

And in London, he used to infuriate me by pointing out every prostitute in the street. When he was there for a military conference, he wistfully suggested that he might be seduced by a sexy lady spy. Once, we were having dinner with his colleagues, and my father reported that a girl had 'solicited' him in Soho. He noted with a mix of prurience and disapproval, 'She was so young! She said she was twenty, but I don't know . . .'

Then he added in a waggish voice, 'I guess as soon as my back is turned, my daughter's going down to Soho . . .'

There are things that daughters can't tell fathers. And when I moved in with John Muckle – saved – my father's heart was broken. 'Why would he buy the cow when he can get free milk? I'm just old-fashioned.' And I would watch Sheldon eat, his jellyfish frame and gobbling making him cartoonish. He was a father made for children four to eight, a father I'd outgrown. And I – in my worn-out Triumph motorcycle T-shirt, torn black leather mini-skirt, scowling at nothing as I turned into the restaurant to meet him – was a kind of person he would never know. A fruitcake.

And my mind would guiltily sketch a different father, one who could be real in the aftermath of grief and rape. My angry thoughts would be the memories of his angry youth. My dramas would be the first few scenes of his more epic narrative, whose meaning he would know, whose happy ending he would demonstrate. Of course this paragon-father couldn't exist.

'Oh, well!' Sheldon would say, lifting his fork in the air like a conductor's baton to signal levity. 'Maybe I should just go to a lady of the night!'

7

The Castle of Fathers

The order of events

A grey chill London evening in our squat lit by gas fires, the white letter in my hand; I'm trembling with father endorphins and hope. The letter includes photographs of my siblings and my father's home. It invites me to LA.

I go tell Amos, and he looks up from his reading of Bataille and starts an argument. I call him unsympathetic, almost crying as if that's a terrible thing to say. Then we make tea and are in sudden accord, tender, laughing about the incidence of fathers where no father was ever sought, until we fuck; how sweet a single hour can be when nothing's right in your life. We go to America three months later, landing in Boston to see Sheldon, then driving west.

The car was from a 'drive-away' firm – one that delivers cars to people who've moved cross-country and don't want to drive themselves. It was a hundred-dollar deposit plus gas and I drove all the way because Amos had never learned how to drive. I don't remember the trip. We must have eaten truck-stop burgers, we must have slept in the car. We must have fought all night while following the tired red eyes of some truck's taillights. But I remember arriving on the horror eight-lane highway into Los Angeles, bumper to bumper juggernauts doing 80, and it's roasting hot. We have the windows down to smoke and the air is thick as swill with dirt, exhaust, and groaning noise. It's like tunnelling through a war movie in our little car. Then we've somehow been flicked off onto a hill where yellow sun nests silent in dry grass. There's no one else around. The roads twist up and out and teeter along the edge of cliffs.

We find the paternal gates, tucked into a long expanse of high whitewashed adobe wall. The driveway's not that long. It isn't acres of feudal realm, it could be worse. Then we're scrambling from the car, in filthy sodden clothes, T-shirts showing blazes of sweat from the hot drive. We're at the castle door. The door is huge, its wood is dark and huge-grained as if hewn from a tree on Jupiter. And I press the doorbell while my Amos stands back putting one friendly paw hand on my shoulder. Saying, 'Fuck this, Sasha,' loud, to cheer me. Then my father opens the door.

The instant I lay eyes on him, I've known him all my life. He is my father; a stranger who looks more familiar than anyone else in the world so far. A small, muscular man, about my height, with my bright-dark intensity, he has a focused squint, he's bearing down on some recalcitrant thought that doesn't stand a chance. He has dark freckles; rounded nice-guy features; has my face like me.

Real father: expository

Unlike Sheldon, my real father wanted to be my father. Primarily (and ever after, unforgettably) he tracked me down. That fact surrounds him with the god glow of the saviour male. He is striding towards me through the wreckage of my early life, a thunderbolt in each hand. My problems scatter.

The castle of the photo was really a mansion called a castle sometimes, lightly, for its castellated tower. Nonetheless the place was gorgeous, vast, pristine. That visit was a tour of make-believe, and the mist of mansioned wealth and Hollywood drugged me in the early days. I didn't understand much about my father for a long time. I distrusted him because of his money; I feared him because our resemblance felt uncanny. Every year, I would spend a week on tiptoe in his ivory scornful mansion. Being there felt like being filmed, and I wanted to leave as if my life were at stake. Then I'd leave, none the wiser.

When we met, it was a time for him when life had had the thorns and glitter sanded down into a right integrity. He was forty-eight; his children grown and gone, his second wife the ideal partner he would never leave. He was settling down to tend his garden, think; to bring to consummation his life's work. Finding me was part of that. I was an adult, and presumably ready to meet him, at the moment he was ready for me.

A father is bigger than you – and the scale of his nature was the wonderful thing. There was room in him, he was the castle of fathers; my father was an effortless leap over anyone's head. He was the father who gave good advice;

who helped in any emergency; who knew best. He was the father fathers want to be.

It took about four years, then I adored him. I loved my three half-siblings, too; they were always bewitching ideals of brother, sister, in my eyes. My love for them was something from the blood, a doom therefore. It was blood in its oceanic guise, its god mask. It meant, You are not you, you are a fragment of the generations that hold you in their web. When a thread of the web is plucked, you sing with love. The singing is your true name.

For a moment – a year – it was pure rescue. My father and I could speak of 'having worked to build a relationship' in the confidence that the job was done. And with my new real parents, my life story was rewritten from page one. The adopted childhood was relegated to an unlit strand of parallel history. There was no need for cognitive therapy to tweak my opinion of myself: I was a different person, the issue of a happy family, a fruit of luck. The standard blithe traits followed of themselves.

I, the girl at thirty, was bunched muscle with soft, small breasts/ass attached, dry flyaway hair, a face. I was paling, not exactly ageing, like a shirt washed many times but never worn. Opened out, my body was thin and stringy, the picture of hungry. In a bad photograph, wet cat. I was seldom opened out. I tended to scroll towards the foetal position; head down, shoulders in, arms crossed. I'd draw my feet up even onto an office chair. I wore my wretch costume, Triumph T-shirt etc., most days, and in a mansion mirror, I looked jarringly shoddy, like a 99-cent-store object left incongruously on the polished floor. I looked like vandalism of that house. Even in the year, the moment, I belonged there, it was through grace not works. I was a real daughter through my father's caprice.

And I didn't want to be a daughter. I didn't know how, and I just couldn't. I wanted to be his friend, but I was his daughter, end of story. And sometimes it was like being an inanimate object, like a chair, uncannily, hopelessly, in love with a human being. I was turned to wood by his good gaze.

Then my real father became the problem. That is the story arc.

In a nutshell; epistolary

Dear [my real father],

    Thank you. Thank you.
I am sorry.
Here's my trivial news. (List follows.)
I will come to visit again soon. Thanks for offering to pay for the ticket, but I think I can manage it on my own, or I will do my best, although there is no way I can pay for it on my own. I'm sorry. Thank you.

    With all friendly consideration,

*   *   *

Dear [my real father],

    Thank you. I am sorry. Trivial news.
How frightened I am of you, how much I miss you! You pain me somehow – could it be your fault? If it's my fault, I don't know what to do.

    Sorry.

    Love,

*   *   *

Dear [my real father],

Thank you. I am sorry.

I realised too late I missed your birthday, and that I behaved very badly at the restaurant, and [list follows]. I didn't mean any harm. I know that doesn't help at all, but I'm not really sorry. Sorry.

Trivial news.

Love,

*   *   *

Dear [my real father],

How I love you. Never contact me again, forget it.

I will repay the money I owe you when I can, I'm sorry that it may be many years.

I can't stand this another moment, sorry. Thank you.

Yours,

Or, metaphorically

A castle where every single person is your father. You can't walk down a hall without encountering your father. You can't help feeling the fathers are sick of running into you. It's their castle. Something about how love is a palace where you don't feel welcome, certain loves, the ones you care about so bad you're bleeding from the ears with rage. Definition of a broken heart. All fathers watching you, nonplussed and nice, not having done anything wrong. Of course you're welcome. You're their daughter.

A smiling father by the fountain, a father calling me from the entrance hall downstairs. The gazebo father and the poolhouse father exchange a worried glance. Aren't there more fathers now than when I went to bed last night? I cover my eyes with my hands to remember loneliness. Somewhere there is an anti-paradise where no one cares about me, a quiet hell where nothing ever gets done. It was so great when misery could be unselfconscious.

Every time we speak, it's as if I've brought him candy, saying, 'Here, I've brought you candy,' and he thanks me for the beautiful flowers. In his hands, the candy looks like flowers. I want to cry and swear. I go straight out to get more candy, *even though the candy couldn't have mattered less*. A hundred times, multiplied by every father in the castle. It was probably flowers. At last, in frustration, I bring him toads, not even good toads, bad toads. What will happen? I wonder, edgy with bravery, almost aroused. What could happen? My father's understandably upset; all the fathers are. 'Bad toads? Why would you do that?' they ask, and I have no answer. The toads hop at the lid of their container, bopping themselves, leaving smears of poison. I am sorry, so damn sorry, my poor head beats red with wrath. I say, 'But I blame you.'

Because having a father made me want a father. Sheldon never acted much like a father, leaving me in peace. This new father held out the possibility of father – then it was a castle full of them fathering through me uselessly while I said, 'It was *candy*,' angry for no reason. 'I don't *feel* welcome.' The good times, our intense discussions and our jokes, made me want a father more, pathetically, wandering down a castle corridor pining, in a terrible mood and I would look out at a jacaranda in blossom, made of father-stuff, an unattainable grace, and all LA was fatherish golden in my eyes, its black palm silhouettes at the horizon, so like daisies, springing sideways like a father abseiling down the cliff of that blue love sky I can never touch.

But in many ways, our problems were like problems decent fathers typically have with unremarkable children; in so many ways, there is nothing to tell. And it is never the right time to tell it. My father is a good man. I'm proud to be his daughter. We don't see each other now, so to talk about him would necessarily be to talk behind his back. It would only be a prolonged cry over spilt milk, spilt through my own fault. My father is a private person; he doesn't want his family life made public. If I knew anything, I would know that. And I don't know anything. Consequently, it would be vain, presumptuous, to say.

The order of events

Then we just left. The castle and its fathers vanished. They became a foreign principle; Amos set up as interpreter and expounded it, desultorily, as our Greyhound bus wormed through LA, past strip malls, strip clubs, past sun-bleached apartment buildings named Bel Air, The Palms, Toulouse. The buildings cleared away like clouds at last, and we were in a sunlit bus in a different story like a children's story in which we were rocked into somnolence, riding the yellow hills to Santa Cruz. We were off to meet my mother for the first time. We stepped out into a dusty Greyhound station, doors all open to the sainted California scent of sun and ocean, drying grass; a promised land. My task was to find my mother, of whom I had never seen even a photo. The crowd thinned quickly, sorting into types as each group found its car. Sally, left behind, was like a distillation of all possible people. She walked up and was exactly right. In retrospect, my father was exactly right for me. He was no threat, no foreign principle; he was mine, the reason I liked poetry and running, and I told myself to remember that for next time as it left my mind.

'I'm the sham husband,' Amos said.

Sally said, 'We did it!'

8

Fortune City

Sham husbands

If I still had no money at the time I met my parents, the key reason was that I'd chosen Amos Weisz not Richard Jones. I chose the sexy madman, not the brainy homely man who cared, who earned, with whom I could be happy. It was the syndrome of the debutante disowned for running off with the saxophone player, the cautionary tale whose heroine dies in penury, scorned; although, in our times, my choice is held to be the moral one. It's 'love'.

I 'loved' Amos Weisz right off. I wanted to fuck him constantly. Once I knew his father had killed himself, we were like comrades, too. I married him after he complained about my asking other men to marry me for the UK passport. I'd thought it would be tasteless to propose to Amos, given we were living together. The helpful upshot was, he proposed to me.

The effect on us of marrying was uncanny. We became like Siamese twins who shared a heart, against our will.

Richard Jones I'd known since the beginning, almost as long as Will. He and Will and Chris Paige shared a house in Stamford Hill, and I'd fetch up there needing a place to stay and hide in corners a couple of days too scared to talk to anyone. Jones was laconic, unflappable, with a scorpion wit, a fell presence like The Brain; while Chris and Will were just pretty-boy bad boys. They'd be passed out drunk with nameless passed-out-drunk chicks while Jones sat up *sans chick* plotting world domination because he was skinny and ginger and couldn't pull. Jones played jazz drums in some ensemble where the 'drums' were contraptions he built out of junk and had at with a spanner. He had been a choirboy at school, Will always said: you were supposed to know what *that* meant.

Then they lost that house and I didn't see Jones for years.

Out of nowhere, Jones and I met up for a drink and fell into bed one night. By daybreak we were in some intense relationship; Jones kissed me for literally hours, until I had scabs on my chin from his ginger stubble. The other hours we talked; Jones was falling for me, and it was clearly the story of the sensitive boy who develops a hard protective shell, but reveals his dewy soul to the girl of his dreams. Except I wasn't falling in love with Jones. I was only having a break from life in some Jones kingdom like an underwater kingdom where all the people were like his friend Kurt with the squatted office building where Kurt lived spread over eight floors contriving supercomputers to hack into MI5 and playing jazz bassoon or something – or like the Iraqi woman so scarred by Muslim treatment of women, she'd become a kung fu black belt and would pick up men, get them to drive her to a secluded spot, and beat the shit out of them, to get her own back.

We broke up once, then got back together the night I first met Amos. Will and Jones and Amos and I were drinking together at the Star and Garter. Will saw me cosy with der Weisz, whose matinee-idol looks pissed anyone off. Will tugged my elbow, saying to me and Richard,

'Look, fuck off, I know you two want to talk to each other. You haven't seen each other in ages. Go on! Don't hang around with us, go have a drink by yourselves . . .' which ended with me and Jones sitting on my floor back in the all-night kiss. Jones said, 'I love you.' And I said it back, I kissed him back: it was a spur-of-the-moment misstep. On the spur of the moment, things just happened, it was like being on a horse that knew you didn't know how to ride. You'd tug this way and that to show you were still involved. The horse went where it liked, just putting its ears back irritably.

Since Jones and Amos were old friends, it was callous of me to sleep with Amos. I'm aware of that. I wasn't aware of it then: I was genuinely callous towards the opposite sex at twenty-five. I'd been through all that prostitution/rape, those teen years, and my attitude was: I am David, and you are Goliath. You hurt me, that's cowardly; my hurting you is an exploit. Everything's fair in love and war, when I say so.

I asked Amos out, but the date was in other ways conventional: in a wine bar, meet at seven. It was my first normal date with someone who wasn't some middle-aged Argentine or Arab who had picked me up in the street saying he was a polo player and did I want to be in a video he was producing, go in his sports car to the most exclusive French restaurant in the city, and here's a watch; that kind of date I'd had at eighteen, before the prostitution killed my interest.

I didn't know how to date. I wore a leather mini-skirt and tiny halter top: the point, I thought, was to be attractive.

Amos brought Richard Jones.

They'd spent the day together at the Anarchist Book Fair. Jones was already beginning to come down with a flu that would be lasting and serious, that would play its role in the events then brewing. He was largely silent through the evening. Amos bantered about the book fair and its tables offering photocopied bomb recipes; Jones, with his acidic stare, watched us barely get along together, possibly nursing *Schadenfreude*, it was tough to know what scary-smart, phlegmatic Jones thought ever. I sat near-silent worrying he had spilled the beans and Amos wasn't going to fuck me. And Jones wasn't. I would never see either of them again.

Jones hadn't spilled any beans. Jones aka Sickman – a man who treasured Derrida and Lacan *because* he found them hollow and pernicious – played a subtler game than that. Amos, in fact, with ingenious anti-tact began to talk sex pretty soon and flirt; Jones observing slumped, his flu exhausting him. At last, Amos progressed to saying he was right-handed sexually; his right nipple and testicle responded more to stimulation. He asked if I had sexual handedness.

Jones said, 'Yes, bollocks,' sharply over this. 'I think I need to be getting home. Coming?' He looked at Amos pointedly as if they'd discussed this. Amos said, *Yeah, right then*, they would catch the Northern Line together, but in the street he reconsidered and offered to walk me home.

Jones stalked off solitary in the frail November rain. Amos and I walked back to the polytechnic halls of residence.

There in bed, I considerately attended more to Amos's right side, to his glee. He'd won round one. He'd invented the handed sexuality on the spot, assuming I'd sleep with him. He wanted to see if I'd go gullibly for his right. Maybe he wouldn't have slept with me at all if not to spring that trap. Or else the joke was an excuse to sleep with me – Amos was driven to reject or humiliate the women he wanted, because to want them made him feel unmanned.

From these motives, he next said, 'If we keep seeing each other, just so you know, I want this to be an open relationship.'

I said, 'Good.' I was already sleeping with his best friend, I couldn't lose that game.

We cried truce then and talked about everything. Like fourteen-year-old new best friends, we traded our most intimate thoughts and feelings. Neither of us had ever met someone whose same-sex parent committed suicide, before. It made us seem like soulmates, or we really were soulmates because of it.

Amos's father, Josef, took an overdose when Amos was nine – one so massive it had been a feat to swallow the myriad pills before losing consciousness. Josef had been a professor of Judaica, a protégé of Gershom Scholem, a thinker. Still his travails in life were legion. Amos's father had excellent pretexts for killing himself.

He'd lost his family to the Nazis, and fled to Israel as a thirteen-year-old alone. His ship had been shelled by the British, but managed to land its passengers alive. As a young adult he'd fled compulsory service in the Israeli army – that Palestinian war Josef found grotesque, nihilistic, so he left his place as the rising academic star in Jerusalem and brought his first wife Miriam to England. That Miriam, a mathematician, suffered badly from the change. In fact, she slowly fell into schizophrenia until she raved and couldn't be left alone. Josef signed the papers for the then fashionable cure, a frontal lobotomy. Afterwards, Miriam was only fit to be shipped back to mother; she'd become a ruined thing that only ate and slept.

In later years, Josef progressed from taking too many sedatives, to suspecting his new wife (Amos's mother) of plotting with the KGB, to thinking the execution of Hungarian resistance leader Josef Dudas was aimed at him because they had the same first name, to suicide.

I was comfortably seated on Amos's thighs while he sat back against the pillows, telling his tale in a tone so earnest it sounded naive; now he hushed and took my hand. He looked at it, its veined back, and we heard his silence patterned by sounds from other rooms of the halls of residence, a symphonic murmuring. I was looking at my old Smith Corona manual typewriter. Beside it lay my biological father's first letter, which I'd received the week before. A page in the typewriter had *Dear [real father]* on it, in that fifties typewriter typeface, the letters thickly hung with genteel serifs like epaulettes. *Dear [real father]* was as far as I'd got.

'Do you believe in life after death?' I asked Amos idly. I was thinking about it as if the right answer was there, on the tip of my tongue. The knobbly shadow of the typewriter keys spilled onto the floor.

'Of course there's life after death,' Amos said. 'They would never let us off that easily. That's why I would never off myself. I'm too afraid that after death it's more of the same.'

'Reincarnation?'

'No! That's bad enough. A disgusting prospect. No, as if nothing had happened,' he said mournfully. 'The same day, the same mug of tea, the same armchair.'

He told me a nineteenth-century mystic Hasid had proposed this as God's reprisal for suicides. No escape, bugger your pitiful attempt at escape; door slammed. Amos wouldn't risk that. He preferred to forge ahead in the hope that death would kill him, rather than risk being lodged eternally in his present life.

I said, 'It doesn't seem likely, though. You can't believe that literally.'

He said, 'Oh, you'd be amazed what I would believe.'

Then he frowned and touched my face, pondering. His dreamy eyes went woebegone. I had looked back at the typewriter keys, at my father in the shape of two crisp sheets of paper folded in thirds, when he said, in a tone of complaint, 'You *look* like me.'

'We have the same features,' I assented, factual. I looked at him, wondering if my father would look like him. I said, 'We're both half Jewish and half German.'

'Jewish on the side of the father,' he said. '*Mischlinge*. And you mean we're both pretty. So be it! But I'm prettier.' He frowned for a moment, looking at the sheepskin rug on my floor. He said, 'I wasn't going to come back with you tonight.'

'You brought Jones, right.'

'Oh, that,' he said as if Jones's presence on our date was a contemptible detail. '*That* was just to piss you off. I'd decided not to have anything to do with you. Jones said you were mad, and I went along with it out of my repellent docility.' He looked at me with his characteristic ponderous green-eyed tender candour, commented, 'I liked you, actually.'

And he told an exemplary story about when he was up at Cambridge. One of the popular boys, the petted sons of the landed gentry, threw a party for his beautiful sister; a flaxen-haired and radiant English angel Amos fell in love with at first sight and shadowed, fruitlessly, all night, vexing her until the brother confidentially asked him to piss off. He'd been pigeonholed as the pushy Jew, thought Amos; the salacious Yid. Finally, wobbly drunk and broken-hearted, he went home with a chubby brash Nigerian girl,

Jenny. Amos and Jenny were together then two years – and Jenny was a good egg, good in bed, a joy, said Amos. Been good for him. Wonderful woman.

The first morning after, Jenny got up and said to him, 'Would you like tea?'

He said, 'How do you know what you'd like?'

Since Jones hadn't told Amos about us, I didn't. It went on that way two weeks. The secrecy made Amos my main lover, somehow; he was the one I cheated on. That could have meant Jones was taboo, therefore sexier, but it didn't. Jones understood that very well.

At last, one night, I was out on a date with Jones with all his work friends, and Amos showed up.

'Will said you'd be here,' he said to me in all innocence. 'Do you want to come to my place after? Hi, Richard.' (Will would crow at me later, 'Classic! You've got to admit that was brilliant cuntery. Chumps!')

Jones had flu; he'd been looking bony and dilapidated, all night. Now he said he was feverish, he ought to be getting home. Could he have a word with me, outside, first?

Amos gave me pondering looks as I followed his old friend downstairs. By the time I hit the pavement, I was cross with nerves. Jones was supposed to be on my side. We were meant to be keeping these balls in the air together.

I said, 'What? Seriously.'

Jones said to me, icy and exhausted, 'Look. Are you coming home with me, or are you going with him?'

I said, 'Richard, come on. Amos doesn't know. It's impossible.'

'Are you coming home with me, or are you going with him?'

'Him, then.'

'Right. Then I'll never speak to you again,' Jones actually said.

I said, 'Fine,' with a brisk sarcasm dulled by fear. I took a deep breath to get my balance. He couldn't be serious. But Jones had already turned and he was walking away.

I took a step to follow, but – Amos upstairs – baulked, and watched Jones go thinking he would recant. He would fall prey to sentimentality or just sense.

He didn't. For years thereafter – even when we lived together at the squat – Jones quietly behaved as if I didn't exist.

Comeuppance/bliss

So Amos and I embarked on our 'married' 'love', a *folie à deux* much truer than real love; more unpremeditated. We spent our days trying to unclothe the soul just in case it was there. I prayed on my knees to see if God existed. Amos followed the precepts of a nineteenth-century mystic rabbi who exhorted, 'We must sin *more strongly.*' Mankind might be empty clothes, it might be a flatulent scarecrow; clay with a word drawn on its forehead. Or it might be gods and galaxies on a head-of-a-pin of soul. This question was all there was; so all day long we doubted and believed all creeds from radical anarcho-syndicalism to Islam. It was a period like living in the nonsense landscape of twentieth-century poetry; morbid, euphoric, finally possibly meaningless by design.

My Amos was a heart-throb then; tall with unshaven-gorgeous looks; green-eyed like a hero of pulp romance. He played the violin, wore black suits rumpled, drank and drank. Had a gentle, sensitive face so keenly thoughtful it seemed stunned. Thoughtful with an amazing thought; rapt with revelations was how Amos looked. When he spoke, my handsome wretch of a lover was ostentatiously brilliant, always. He'd gone to Cambridge on a maths exhibition, then switched to philosophy; he knew all that, I was the roughneck, ignoramus, (charitably) the auto-didact. What are you thinking, Amos? He was thinking about the algebraic logic of Breuer, he was devising a Riemannian economics, was so smart he was insane and all his three-ring-circus thought for nothing. And he was really gentle seldom; never sensitive once. Dreamy Amos didn't mind if mankind suffered. Hadn't that always happened? Weren't those kitchen-sink concerns, in fact; the province of the women? On this point we bitterly fought a lot; one of his poems on me starts with 'Oh you squally'.

We scarcely worked. We lived on scraps, we borrowed, we got handouts from our parents. For one fat year, we lived off money from a flat that Amos sold, an inheritance squandered on free time for thinking, talking, nothing, all over Europe.

We read all day at tables and, at home or in bars, our world was red wine bottles and coffee mugs posed off-centre on the rings from prior bottles and mugs; cigarette ash worked into wood grain – we saw nothing else for two years. Argued while we understood each other only. We trailed around Lisbon, Avignon, Berlin, in bad used clothes bought by the kilo, eating the cheapest thing on every menu, looking Bambi-like. Real people meeting us drunk in bars chided us and tried to bed us.

I wrote him a poem in Russian and called him Moshik after. He called me Sasha. We had that sloppy loverliness as well, the doting. 'Puppy' was his other nickname; Puppy Moshik, Baby Sasha. And I wrote on the wall of a club in Prague, 'Moshik and Sasha fucked here,' in a drunken flight of boasting. It was true, a restroom fuck. That was one night (after another) of careening sadness, on the 4 a.m. walk home we had a fistfight on an icy bridge. I threw his hat into the river below, he threw my scarf. I punched him. Amos punched me back, we had our only physical brawl, he broke a blood vessel in my eye. The grey Prague streets were empty, looked like they were made of frost and sleep; and we were the only thing awake, the only warm, the one wrong note. And that's what it was like, our marriage, oh so beastly lonely. Besotted by the glamour of being lost, we'd sink however low, we'd still be pretty and soaked with impossible hopes, like starlets. It was just like us to meet my long-lost father in a castle, just like one of our galling affectations.

We tried living in separate rooms, then separate flats, then in adjacent countries; commuting weekends between Germany and the Czech Republic. In East Berlin, he had three girlfriends. In Prague, I slept with a Danish baron, thinking to win that round; when told, he hushed for a moment. Then said, 'Sasha. That's so *sordid*.' We were sordid; Eastern Europe had a sordid, morbid cast for us. The baron gave us gonorrhoea. Amos said his new girlfriends were better lays than me. An Israeli friend of his tried to get a German girl to have a threesome with them by guilt-tripping her, saying, 'My grandmother was a Mengele twin,' which claim was true. The German girl just laughed and left, but I hated them all for laughing. I couldn't match that cynicism. And the sordid, morbid light our dirty windows shed on a wasted afternoon was sometimes all his fault. To him, it was my fault he couldn't go to the dogs outright, sleep on the park bench or the bar-room floor; run loco, like his schizo heroes Hölderlin or Paul Celan, like Dad. Like he did do once I'd gone.

I'd say to him, tetchy, 'Amos, madness in reality is in no way glamorous.'

'Sasha,' he'd say plaintively, 'what else could be?'

What else is there

In the midst of this long love brawl, I began my career, in palsied fits and false starts. I was used to having not quite enough to pay the bills; I aimed for that. I worked as little as possible, to have free time to write, even when I didn't write.

In Prague, I was teaching English, amid the post-Wall infestation of Prague by feckless Americans teaching English. I wasn't exactly one. They weren't much more like me than feckless Slovaks were. Still, I hung with the American kids while they made gourmet pizza and drank gourmet beers and traded celebrity gossip and missed grad school.

In that crowd, the done thing was to bemoan the American influence. Sometimes it seemed the Americans had come to Prague expressly to have intense conversations about US cultural imperialism. The most extravagant show of expatriate soul-searching I witnessed was at an American-owned place called Asylum, where they had bad American bands and showed bad American art. The atmosphere was childhood-nostalgia – peanut butter and jelly sandwiches served on Sears plates to post-grads playing Candyland on child-sized plastic tables. The bad band playing was doing a series of horrible original songs. But at the end of the set, they played a Nick Cave cover, and people hushed to listen. That song got the night's first round of applause.

Stung, the front man rounded on the audience. He was a gorgeous bearded bicepped creature with a rag tied artlessly around his glossy head, and clearly used to some adulation on these points. He let rip that 'This is fucking typical of Prague where shit is really ruined by all you brainwashed American kids! It's so totally Americanised. We came today from Krakow, and I'm fucking devastated by the difference. There it's real! It's got real *art* going on there, it was fucking life-altering! All *you* want to do is listen like sheep to cover songs instead of experiencing anything challenging. Wake up, people! You have to sacrifice to keep life authentic!' he screamed in climax. 'You have to be willing to cut your throat for art!' He flailed his finger across his throat in a wild slashing gesture.

The audience was muttering and whining. One of the managers, a little cute guy like a gerbil in a baseball cap, sprang onto a table and said, 'This is a wonderful opportunity! Let's open up debate and really *talk* about these issues!'

So the Americans on the stage and the Americans in the audience debated the American influence while the sprinkling of Czechs among them drank beer paid for by the Americans.

At least they could teach English; I could not. Afraid of strangers, I would stammer and sweat and lose my thread. There were complaints to the school, which made me panic more. Factoring in Amos and his three girlfriends in Berlin, I was delusional with anxiety, and in my time off, I was trying to finish a novel about atrocities, set in Siberia, that would not get good.

After a month in Prague, I said to Amos, 'Do you think this teaching job could be making me lose my soul?'

He said, 'Yes, I think it is.'

That woke me from my mood. 'Christ's sake, Mosh! I didn't mean that seriously!'

'You asked, that's my opinion,' Amos said with gravitas. 'You've been different since you started that job. Your spirit brightness isn't the same.'

To salvage my 'spirit brightness', Amos offered to set up editing work for me with a Berlin firm of translators. That gave me the excuse I needed to quit the teaching. But the editing work fell through, and two weeks later, Amos fell in love with someone else, as he informed me over the phone in mournful tones. He couldn't be in love with two women at one time, he said. Furthermore, he'd had a dream in which we were two Marx Brothers riding horses into a punch bowl. When he woke up, he realised our relationship was going nowhere.

I returned to London. There I got my everlasting typing job at Tellex Monitors.

Tellex was the job artistic wastrels got in London then. It was a den of resting actors, starving artists, over-educated failures. The work was recording and transcribing radio and TV programmes. Suppose the Energy Secretary got interviewed on the *Today Programme*. The Department of Energy would order a transcript, to pore over every word and craft a more Orwellian message next time round.

Transcribers like me sat all day in fat headphones. The transcripts were verbatim, lovingly preserving the ums and ahs. It was a fascinating education in how inarticulate speech can be while passing muster. Some politicians never uttered a meaningful sentence. It would be, 'I was pointing out in the event of some contingently happening that might interfere with goals achieved, and they are achieved in 81 per cent of regions, which our Opposition has been forced to capitulate, as you will surely agree.'

The pay was low, and hourly. If the work ran dry, the

employees got sent home. In a bumper year, you could earn enough to live.

Work made my life much worse. Now that I entirely supported myself, I worked through colds and stomach flus and migraines. I worked with only one contact lens left and one eye shut. Earphones on, I would enter a diluted dulled hypnotic state as the whole day passed without me. Months passed. Sometimes I had rent. Sometimes I just slept at the friend's flat who lived closest to Tellex. Sometimes I lived with Amos's mother.

At Tellex, all the national newspapers were provided so we could check spellings of names. They were generally strewn about open to the job ads. It was traditional for Tellex employees to compose job applications whenever work was slow. I was no exception. And for years I received rejection letters for every entry-level position advertised in London.

I left sometimes to do temp work for a higher hourly rate. But I would pine for Tellex, where I could appear dripping wet from cycling in through sheeting rain, where everyone was in the same becalmed boat. It wasn't that much more money, I would start thinking, wrongly. Then there was a time I went door to door, soliciting money for Friends of the Earth. It would be useful to society, I thought, but I raised near nothing and felt bad for taking commission, and I was back at Tellex.

In a holiday from all reason one year, I joined a team of gamblers. I got the job from an ad in LOOT: *Professional gambler's assistant wanted. International travel, all expenses paid, £120/week.* I went to a rendezvous with the gambler, a Canadian former civil engineer who was small but in good shape for a man of sixty-three. He'd been playing casino blackjack for fifteen years, and the job was real, the interview was like a fantastic dream. However, he had the oily, overly plausible manner of someone trying to get in a young girl's pants.

He hired a team of four young women and tried to sleep with us in Mississippi, Kuala Lumpur and, for a brief improbable fortnight, Kathmandu, where we left town in the middle of a general strike, and where the casino electricity flickered on and off and everything would be sunk into darkness for a silent heartbeat. Then the lights would plunge back on and the poised, sari-clad croupier would be smiling, dealing the next card to the beat of the on-switched light.

Playing blackjack professionally requires intense, intelligent concentration on the same cards over and over. Sometimes the cards are counted, weighing high against low (high +1, low -1); sometimes sequences are memorised. In either case, it requires a narrowing of consciousness not unlike meditation, for hours at a stretch.

I saved £120 a week while we lived three to a room in extended-stay hotel rooms. The team members rotated rapidly, kaleidoscopically, as girls quit, losing patience with the miserly lech boss, who'd dyed his hair pitch black and wore it in a stiff frizz bob, and who had a pair of white trousers that he wore with black underpants showing through. When he hired the team, he'd had some harem fantasy going which bore no fruit. Once when we were all playing tennis, another girl said to me, 'Do you think he takes off his shirt to put us off our game?' That was the tone. Meanwhile, the boss grew fanciful, embittered, Lear-like gradually. Began to come back from the men's room haunted, saying, 'I'm an old man . . . oh, my God. That face in the mirror.' Over dinner, he depressed the table with tales of Barcelona brothels and Chang Mai bar whores, trying to weave some mojo. All he got was snotty girls rolling their eyes at the old creep, and no sex, was the bottom line, plans gone awry.

He began to sack the girls on paranoid hunches: Lou was stealing from him, Julaine was. Still the new hires gave no sex. We were not to talk to anyone, meaning men. Those men were casino spies or thugs out to rob our bankroll: to which the yawning ladies rolled their eyes and muttered, out of earshot, 'Somebody's jealous.'

Amazingly, though he travelled at all times with a briefcase packed with hundred-dollar bills, the girls didn't really steal. It was as if all this took place in Victorian times, when such things were unthinkable.

And it *was* like time running parallel to real life, a cloistered but carefree un-year. In Malaysia, I went running daytimes in the resort's golf course, its greens bulldozed into virgin jungle; silver butterflies and turquoise hummingbirds rose like airs on a flute from banks of tropical flowers as I passed by. We got barred from all the casinos in Mississippi in one day, and were expelled from the Casino Magic's coffee shop in the middle of a chocolate milkshake, frogmarched through the parking lot and warned to never return again, the chocolate milk moustache still wet. We wore disguises that fooled no one and played unconvincing roles. Sometimes the boss posed as a professor, improbably saucily on a casino tour with four girl students. Sometimes we pretended not to know each other for seven hours while sitting inseparably side by side. Clandestine signals ranged from knocking knee against knee to touching the nose. It was shocking how many times you touched your nose in an hour unconsciously, thereby triggering frenzied betting you couldn't forestall without blowing cover.

I learned that playing cards all day is never glamorous

and can't be made less boring; that casinos are inhabited by unhappy baggy-faced Chinese men with sweat-stained shirts, whose piteous cries of 'Picture!' and 'Lucky seven!' make you loathe the world and them for being too nakedly tragic – and never by any tycoons or models. I learned to card count and track aces, and that the slickest legerdemain would only earn a blackjack player a middle-class wage. I learned, finally, listing 'Professional Blackjack Player' on CVs never won you interviews, even on the principle that anyone must be curious.

Then I was back at Tellex Monitors. 'Um, the fiscal roundabout is staying still, in the face of wrongly churlish analysts, yes, and I'll say this fairly boldly.'

My second departure from reality was the cat hoax.

I had moved to Gateshead, near Newcastle, in the blighted and jobless North. The man I had fallen in love with there, Steve, had been on the dole time out of mind, like all his friends and their friends and 45 per cent of the neighbour-hood according to official statistics. I got dole too, one theretofore untried solution to the money question. An easy answer, but I couldn't stand the hopeless prospectlessness with no future, the view from the window of eternal rain on trash where feral teens smashed cars' windscreens with scrap metal, dancing to keep their footing in a litter of rotting food, scrap metal, and bones. In that street with no trees, grass, or colour, with the miasmal air of a mildewed dead aquarium, I couldn't live on the dole because it meant living there for ever.

Our house was in Bensham; a huge tumbledown three-storey Victorian, let for £25 a week because the walls were visibly pitted and furred, the plaster crumbling forth with damp. We lived in the one room where the gas fire was.

People were forbidden to visit unless they'd phoned, because next door were heroin dealers. Louts came to their door all hours, and our door by mistake. Any knock might be a wild-eyed sniffling felon poised to shout, 'Where's fucking Neil?' and barge past. These next-door smack dealers were a married couple, the parents of five scream-faced brats who wandered the streets with actual clubs like Homo Erectus young.

Despite the interdiction, our friend Michaela's five-year-old, Hannah, used to drag her mother to the door and shrill into the letter slot, 'Vicar! Steve the Vicar!' until we came. (Steve got the nickname 'Vicar' when he played in bands. He was in a duo with the painfully jokey name 'More T. Vicar'. One pub landlord misread the T as a plus sign, and wrote it on the chalkboard 'More and Vicar'. Of the duo, Steve was the obvious vicar. He was balding, bearded, slight; Steve looked like a meeker, more ginger Lenin, or a Church of England vicar. He began to dress as a vicar at Halloween, buying pukka vicar garb from the Church of England staff store. Soon everybody but his parents called him Vicar.) So Hannah and mum Michaela would camp out on our sitting-room floor for hours, smoking grass which Steve (like everyone else we knew) grew in the attic. Hannah built whole castles out of empty Silk Cut packets and jabbered, breathless, silly with a little-blonde-angel contact high, while other mums and dads arrived and rolled new spliffs and told old stories.

Apart from entertaining, Steve spent his prospectless days composing and recording classical music on a Casio keyboard. 'This is a little something I wrote at the end of the eighteenth century,' he'd say, introducing one of his whimsical, fragile, Mozarty, pieces. Another thing Steve said, and wished he'd never said, was, 'Pussycat owners are mad. They'll buy fucking anything cat-themed. If I marketed my music by saying it was written for cats, I'd be a millionaire.'

The friends who stopped by that afternoon agreed. It was, 'I'll be your valet, Vicar.' And, 'Get a helicopter with the millions, eh? In the shape of a cat.' And, 'Bags I answer the pussycats' letters.'

Still half as a joke, I wrote the CD cover copy. It claimed Steve was a composer of film soundtracks. Over the years, he'd noticed his cat Ralph responded to certain tunes by coming to lie on top of the piano purring. The copy was a hit with our stoned friends.

By then, I'd got the bit between my teeth. *Music for Pussycats* was born. At no time did Steve or myself feel doubt as to whether cats listen to music, which cats do not, we knew. The only grain of truth in the story was that Steve once had a cat named Ralph, five years before, of which cat he had been excessively fond.

Sheldon invested $500 in the enterprise. It was the only thing I'd ever done that goofy Sheldon unequivocally liked. He kept saying, 'That's wonderful. Music for cats!' I found the cheapest CD duplicating company in the North-east and bought spools of the cheapest packing materials. Steve gave the musical pieces cat-themed names like 'Sheba, the Desert Cat', and 'Shiver Me Whiskers'. An ad in *Cat World* cost a third of our capital. We even went door to door to pet shops, trying to push a point-of-sale stand. The pet shop owners shooed us off, impatient as if cat music hawkers were a perpetual nuisance. At last, I wrote a press release; that was where the real trouble began.

The story first ran in the *Newcastle Journal*. Reporters came to Bensham and did a shoot of Steve posed with a stray cat who'd coincidentally followed us into the house that week half-starved. We explained she wasn't 'Ralph' (we called the cat 'Pusscat' for simplicity), but they didn't care. 'We'll say it's Ralph, it's easier.' They didn't care that our derelict house was clearly not the home of a composer of film soundtracks. They photographed Steve and Pusscat against a plain white wall and ran the story.

It was picked up by a press agency and recycled in the *Daily Telegraph* and the *Sun*. The *Mail on Sunday* sent their own reporter and photographer, who in their turn took shots of Steve and 'Ralph' and cooked a story out of the press release. Radio programmes interviewed the by now nerve-wracked Steve.

'I feel like a clown,' he told me. 'I wanted people to hear my music, yes. But this is humiliating. I can't stick the lying any more.' He would have stopped answering the phone and waited for the storm to pass. I owed my father $500, though, and the CD had only sold three copies, so far. One row we had while waiting for Radio Leeds to call for a live phone interview ended with me shouting full force, 'What the fuck is wrong with you?' just as the phone rang. Steve went through the interview shaking, green with fatigue.

Cruelly, at this point, producers at *This Morning with Richard and Judy* contacted Steve and asked him to be on TV with Ralph.

As if developing Steve-like scruples, Pusscat vanished the day before. The next-door neighbours amiably loaned us their cat, Lester. A handsome ginger tom, Lester went into the carrier tractably, unfazed by being borne off by strangers. A sleek car hired by ITV took us to Liverpool, where we were put up in a four-star hotel. Steve and I spent an awkward night there trying to enjoy the holiday; by then we could barely talk to each other. Our relationship had foundered amid the uncontrollably mushrooming cat music scam that still paid nothing. We were in the same worn clothes and flapping shoes. We sat in a deserted bar lounge eating steak beneath a potted palm with pop unfeline music playing and mourned our lives, on ITV's dime.

We went to sleep drained. In the morning, Lester was nowhere to be found. We hunted everywhere and called: the cat had vanished. There weren't any gaps in the wall. There didn't seem to be anywhere he could have fit through. I spent the afternoon roaming hotel corridors with bellboys doggedly crooning, 'Buster! Buster!' because I didn't have the heart to correct them.

Steve went on TV alone. The details of that horrible broadcast, during which Richard and Judy sat Steve at a keyboard and tested him against a cat panel, I scarcely can make myself recall. The cats were brought on one by one and deposited on the floor. Steve was alternately instructed to play music cats did like and didn't like. He struck a chord or two, trying to make a loud discordant noise when the music was 'anti-cat'. He looked like death, it was excruciating. After a commercial break in which Steve got too frank, Judy announced on air that the missing cat identified previously as Ralph was Lester and an imposter. A call was sent out to find Lester and restore him to his real and broken-hearted owner, seven-year-old Becky. In the course of the programme, they obtained a photo of the cat to broadcast, and did so repeatedly. (The next-door neighbours, when we got home *sans* cat, said, 'Ooh, never you mind, he'll turn up. Lester does that, he'll be in the walls somewhere. We saw you on that show: it were a right laugh!' Becky chuckled like mad, elated with her fame.)

We rode home utterly silent, dreading our inevitable break-up on top of it all. Lester turned up next day and was driven home in a separate car.

In vindication of cat-lovers: we sold five CDs, total.

Then I was back at Tellex Monitors. 'Every place will be its story. In some regions, the likelihood promises, tomorrow will be another day.'

A temp job and another temp job. A data entry job at *Chambers Legal Directory* involved typing the bios of all the solicitors and barristers in England. I lost my mind from tedium and introduced my own surreal material into the lawyers' lives. (Example: replacing 'Lives in Brighton with her family' with 'Lives in a hollowed-out pumpkin on a trading estate'.) There was no way of tracing the contributions back to me, not officially, but.

I was back at Tellex Monitors. I began to do volunteer work in the evenings, after work. That made it eighty or ninety hours a week of work, not just to pass the time – *you understand, you fucking ungrateful universe?* – but to help mankind. The volunteer work (washing dishes and making beds in homeless shelters, mainly) might have led to paid work, but it didn't. Exhausted and exhausted, I gave that up and I was working onward into the dark and ageing with no hope.

At Tellex.

Tellex. The night shift; often all night no work. Someone had to man the keyboards in case work came. Most nights, I wrote stories. I was writing increasingly tortuous and psycho fantasies about wind-up mouse revolts or intelligent plankton staging micro rebellions or filthy homunculi infesting floorboards in the HQ of failed revolutionists, etc., and taking the bus home shagged out, a shadow of, etc. into the deepening dark.

Here Jones resurfaced.

At the time we were dating, Richard Jones had got a job at a money magazine. The management there had fired the striking staff and hired scabs, anyone who could read, to take their place. Or that was Jones's self-deprecating explanation. He openly stated he was doing it from self-interest; we persisted in believing it was perversity, or even a form of art. Still, within five years of leaving the squat, he was a millionaire, having marched straight through us to success. It was marvellous to us to watch him make one decision after another that profited Jones, unhesitating, effortless, like an adult completing a child's crossword puzzle.

Jones had moved from financial into computer journalism, and risen to editor-in-chief. His magazine won awards and boomed. As the internet bubble began to form and swell, he launched his own web firm.

Fortune City was a virtual community and shopping mall. People could sell merchandise through 'stores' on 'streets' there. It had a thirties gangland theme, and as a promotional stunt, Richard wanted someone to write a mystery in the style of Raymond Chandler. Scenes from the story would be scattered in different parts of town, allowing the reader/browser to piece together the clues by travelling from place to place. Possibly the solution to the whodunnit would vary, depending on your route through town. It was the sort of thing that seemed very cutting-edge then, before it was recognised as unwieldy, pretentious and less interesting than books.

Will told me, 'Do a sample. Jones can't be angry at you now, that was sex crap, that was crap. Just write a couple of pages.'

'I don't know if I can write to order,' I said – and got a couple of Raymond Chandlers from the library later that afternoon and wrote two pages, riffing, not even thinking especially hard, that night. It turned out to be second nature.

Given a template, I could crank out copy for hours at a time without getting tired. I was a natural hack.

Jones liked it. He invited me for a drink to talk terms.

The venue was an early bed bar, though we didn't sit on a bed. People were drinking cocktails mainly, which I hadn't seen before in London; being poor had made me miss one whole sea change in nightlife. This bar already looked like a bar in twenty-first-century Brooklyn: exposed wood, kitsch crushed velvet, overdressed baby bankers sprawled on beds and drinking God knows what, sangria, and looking a little like children dressed in their parents' clothes.

Jones came in looking cordial, unruffled down to the cellular level as if he'd never hated me all those years. He had a prosperous woolly gleam of well-being, like being Jones was a real pleasure. Jones had started lifting weights and had filled out, now had shoulders. His clothes were exactly the right clothes, without straining or conscious vanity because he'd paid top dollar to spend just five minutes in the shop.

The relief I felt at seeing him was like nourishment. Boiled down to: I got to see a friend that happy, shiny with luck. Even a habitually envious mind like mine keeps some people set aside, whose success we treasure, whose prosperity and whose one-night stands with teenaged starlets, even, give us joy. It made me feel all mushy. I wanted Jones to rule the world.

Meanwhile, I had the afflicted, dirtied look of long-term poverty. I was poised on what Will called a 'clothing horizon' – when all your clothes fall apart at the same time. My clothes looked grubby when they were clean. I'd cut my own hair, had for ten years. Although I hadn't markedly aged, I'd changed from a kid who looked street to an adult who looked unwholesome. Most of all, misfortune stank from me. I was what people shun in people.

Jones said that it was really good to see me. And Jones said he could pay me £10 for every hundred words, to start. I felt light-headed because that was a lot of money. To me; it would be all my bad debts. Money for writing, anyway, was like getting paid for nothing, thinking.

Jones bought us a round of drinks, and then we were talking easily because we'd always had a lot to say to each other – though it was like hydroplaning one inch over the talks we'd once had. Like a dream in which you realise you can fly a plane, so you do, but you faintly know you could never fly a plane before. Perhaps I'm not making this clear. I was surprised how much I really loved Richard. I don't know what there is to make clear. The whole nightmare of five years' pointless typing into nowhere was evaporating: meanwhile, Jones was chatting to me as if I fit in his charmed life.

So we talked about Raymond Chandler, and why contemporary mysteries weren't that cool. Jones told me his magazine concept, *Honeymoon Bliss,* which combined the virtue of being commercial with giving its staff five-star vacations. I told him about the plankton rebellion fiction, which Jones of all people was equipped to get. At last, he told me about the girl he was dating, bright and lovely, 'But she's just a little staid. I'm not sure what it is. Predictable or by the numbers.'

'Boring,' I said laughing. Then said, 'Sorry. No.'

'I wouldn't say boring because it's not boring. But, well, boring.' She was meeting him here – he would have to be rude and kick me out then – but I could meet her and judge.

I reflected that Jones did not undyingly want me (such was my impression, though in the next two months, while working at Fortune City, we had drinks a few times, and always talked with the same charmed ease, we got each other's jokes instinctively and I thought it pretty piquant I should want him more now that he was alpha, too late, because it would have been unsporting, tasteless, even to flirt, even if he'd wanted me which I doubted. Then the site was officially launched and shit went mad, there was no time now for pleasant drinks. At last one day Will, whom Jones had appointed accountant of his fledgling empire out of philanthropy probably, warned me, 'Something's off. I got my money out. If you want to get paid, best hassle now, cause Fortune City—' He shook his head, a word to the wise. And since I needed my money, I phoned and phoned, but got no Jones, for weeks, or it could have been a couple of days, time plays tricks when you owe back rent. I freaked out and sent a threatening letter, at which Jones paid, but we weren't friends then (nor did the business fold; its woes were all Will's fabrication, bred from jealousy by beer) – all of which was far from my mind, of course, that night we sat in sweet, surprising accord in the slick Bed Bar).

The boring girlfriend came and sat down breathless, late. A slight and angular pretty brunette in bright red, she said, 'Listen, Richard, I've quit my job. I'm going to Chile for six months to cycle down the Andes with my old friend, Anna, so I won't be around for that thing on the fifth . . .' which slap in the face gave me and Jones much merriment during the brief enchanted life left to our friendship.

9

The Outer Space of Mothers

For about the span of time including my blackjack year and cat music, Sally was working on the joint US/Russian space project. The experiments were designed to be run on space station Mir, and featured the traditional upside-down quail, plants akimbo, and frogs robbed of their Circadian rhythms, languishing in free-fall.

The cosmonauts and astronauts trained together, so the American backbiting got a bracing admixture of Russian mendacity. The Russian officials preferred stonewalling to any other mode of communication, except for lies. Their concept of 'American contribution' was purely monetary. Because they never stated this, the Americans continued with puppyish friendliness to assume cooperation was happening. 'Yevgeny wouldn't actually lie to my *face*,' the Americans would suppose. 'He wouldn't dare, anyway, because he'd be shamed publicly when it comes out.' Yevgeny did not feel shame, he was a former Communist Party member. And no amount of experience could teach the Americans to distrust Russians enough, because it would have hurt their pride to think those nice, hospitable people weren't their friends.

Sally began to fly to Moscow several times a year. Because these flights all left around six in the morning, she always got the same limo driver to the airport, a garrulous, tooth-less man named Mike. He was a handsome devil in his forties, with a screw-loose quality that made him asexual. Over time, she learned that Mike had lost his apartment and was living in a van. She asked if he would like to cat-sit for her during her absences.

Sally's friends (that chorus that speaks for common sense) said she was nuts. Would she be safe? Her stuff! There was something faintly scandalous in the homeless man moving in with the single woman, a hint of eyebrow-raising in the commentary. Sally reacted in her sneaky, stubborn fashion, agonised by shame but going on as if public opinion didn't exist.

After a few months' cat-sitting, Mike moved into Sally's shed full-time. This shed was partly furnished, carpeted, with an electric outlet and a single bed. There was an electric heater, but no insulation. Insects regarded it as part and parcel of their woods, and the bugs that lived there were outdoor bugs: beetles, caterpillars, spiders. The dirt on the floor was soil and redwood fronds. There Mike lived for seven years.

The first year he lost his limo-driving job for driving drunk. He went on to lose a job in a bakery, one at a pizza delivery place, and then his driver's licence. Thereafter, when he wanted to go somewhere, he wrote his destination on a piece of cardboard and stood by the highway. He was ever falling through new cracks of life, a cheery, guileless hobo. Tall dark and handsome to no purpose, Mike would bumble through the house in raggedy clothes with his head down, narrating: 'I'm getting the cat food, first I got to check if the cat food in the refrigerator is all right, it looks all right, now where's the bowl? I'm going to find the bowl, let's look in the cabinet first . . .' Winters, Mike slept in the house on a heap of blankets on the floor, and sometimes, when she was most stressed, Sally would lie on the couch alongside, and let his ceaseless babble lull her to sleep.

She tried to make him useful by assigning him odd jobs, but Mike couldn't keep a task in mind long enough to begin. He would drift off, hitch a ride to the nude beach (his one passion in life) or sit smoking pot in the shed all day, talking to himself about how mad Sally was going to be if he didn't fix those shingles. When Mike had a job, she charged him $200 rent, a cosmetic amount intended to normalise his status: 'This is my lodger.' But Mike forgot to pay or put off paying from month to month.

Sally would say, 'I know I shouldn't react. But it's so frustrating. He's *really* irresponsible!'

And, 'After knowing Mike, I realised there are people who genuinely can't take care of themselves. I mean. He was never going to get any better.'

And, 'The government should just take care of these people! Man. I'm glad I was already left-wing.'

In the Mir years, Sally routed her homeward flights through Europe and took time off with me. It was a rich time of *per diems* that never got fully spent in Moscow. We met in Paris, Rome, or Sally would stop in London for a couple of days. And, as seemed inevitable from the time we discovered we both spoke Russian, she also took me along to Moscow.

I had been to Russia before, on my year abroad at the polytechnic. That was under Gorbachev, when product shortages defined life, and queueing for cheese or sausages was as important a social glue as samizdat newspapers. This was the Yeltsin era: guards with automatic rifles lounged in front of any respectable hotel, any successful business. Scraps of glittery capitalism had grown into the chinks of the elephantine Soviet architecture. A glass shopfront with dainty gilt lettering would appear between two frowning stone facades like a bit of coral reef getting its first toehold on an underwater cliff. The professional classes went unpaid: the space agency itself was paying salaries six months in arrears. All the Russian rocket scientists worked after hours as taxi drivers.

Some days Sally went to supervise trainings by herself, leaving me to wander the streets among the armed men, and sneak into the new too-shiny cafés to order cakes in a faint and timid Russian that made the café workers sigh and look at each other. Just as often she took me with her, though. I'd tag along with a liberty all the more surprising now, post-9/11, when visitors aren't allowed into any NASA facility without prior arrangement.

The second day we drove out to Star City, the Russian cosmonauts' training centre, once a top-secret installation where no foreigner had ever set foot. It was a city in name only: a cluster of twenty-odd institutional buildings in the middle of virgin forest. The drive was spectacular. Moscow has no suburbs; it turns from tower blocks to old growth forest with no intermediate stages. The transition feels like ocean diving: the bleached sunlight on concrete, a blink, then aquatic dusk beneath gargantuan trees. The Russian woods are built on a grand scale, and you expect aurochs and mammoths to browse among the massive trunks, turning a placid eye on the passing cars. Then Star City itself was drab and ugly. Cosmonauts and their families lived on site in concrete blocks, sent their children to school in nearby concrete blocks, and worked in concrete blocks that were like warts sprouting in the magnificent woods.

I don't remember if it was in Star City or in Moscow that we saw the mock-up of the space station. We were given the tour by a cosmonaut, a remarkably handsome man who nonetheless had the hangdog wear in his face typical of middle-aged Russians, and abundant dandruff. The cosmonauts lived in this mock-up for weeks at a time, testing their endurance of close conditions. As a result, the mock-up smelled penetratingly of feet. The tininess of the station was striking. The rooms were about the size of a big dog's cage. To go from one to another, you crawled through a brief tunnel only slightly wider than your body. The whole thing would fit comfortably in the average suburban living room. This in the vastness of space.

Because the lack of privacy caused psychological problems, the station incorporated a place where the cosmonauts could go to be alone. It was a chamber like a narrow shower stall, with a curtain to draw across the door. The cosmonaut demonstrated by getting in and pulling the curtain, and we all burst out laughing at how pathetic it was. Then the curtain was opened and there he was, wearing that half-smile of ostentatious long-suffering which indicates 'the Russian soul'.

I spent one day in the headquarters of the space agency in Moscow – called the Institute for the Study of Biological Sciences to baffle spies. Most of the day we sat in a lab and chatted with the scientists. A mildly retarded man puttered around in the background, nominally a janitor, really an artefact of the Soviet system of hidden unemployment. He pretended to mop around us, staring intently at all the women. From time to time he cornered someone and earnestly asked whether they had any brothers or sisters. He didn't listen to the answer, but fastened on the miracle of getting attention with an air of triumph. Therefore, he could ask the same person about his siblings any number of times. The Russian scientists, long used to this, answered patiently without cracking a smile. The Americans tried politely to start a conversation with the guy, managing at length to extract from him the information that he had a cat with the grand name of 'Pushunya' – or, in English, 'Fluffy'.

At a certain point, I asked for the ladies' room. They sent me off unaccompanied; I slunk off keenly feeling my status as a person who could be spying. I felt wicked wandering down the hall, it was that specific taboo joy you had in the Soviet Union, when the totalitarian whole was composed of innumerable little anarchies. Bringing my little widow's mite of cussedness, I quietly wrote 'Sandy + Steve' on the stairwell wall in ballpoint: I was still with Steve the Vicar then, and I thought knowing it was there would please him.

Then I stood in the corridor, waiting for Stalinist lightning to strike me down. The silence was clean like sweet mint. I thought, 'A family is all right, if it's your family.' And, 'Because this is a different kind of thing altogether from Sheldon and Louise.'

10

What Kills You

I misremember this scene as taking place outdoors in blazing sunlight, the street dust harsh in my lungs. It would have actually been the London Heathrow arrivals area. Sheldon came out in a wheelchair she was pushing: my heart skipped a beat. It was my father's mortality acted out, as clearly as if the Grim Reaper were pushing the chair.

By the time I caught my breath, he was rolled to a point in front of me, at waist height.

'Hi!' my father cried up from his wheelchair. 'This is Diane, Sandy! Diane, meet my daughter!'

'Sandy, I heard so much about you,' she said impartially. 'You're as pretty as your father said.'

'I got this wheelchair,' Sheldon said, 'cause they offer them to you if you're too slow. Now I never want to give it up. It's cool! You just roll along!'

She was a strapping six-foot blonde in her late thirties. Her doughy features gave the impression of good nature, and her fair hair was curly, short, a seventies cut. She wore a denim dress that was almost Christian in its dowdiness. Then and later, she seemed like any townie girl who'd gone to my high school, no one in particular.

'So,' my father said redundantly, absently, 'Sandy – meet my wife.'

What you get, if you get that far

About the time I moved north to Gateshead, Sheldon retired to Florida. He'd bought a basic bungalow in West Palm Beach in a gated community. His home was still a dirt lot when he put the money down. When built, the houses there were the same house in four different orientations and five pastel shades, paced by evenly spaced palm trees of identical height. At the heart of the development was a deserted recreation centre with pink umbrellas reflected crisply in a turquoise pool. The uniformity and tidy antisepsis of the place suggested a post-human exurb, maintained in its end state by unthinking robots.

'It's nice!' my father said. 'The garage is gigantic. I'll be glad to never climb those stairs again. It's seventy degrees in Florida now!'

When my aunt Ruth heard Sheldon was hiring a moving truck to ship his furniture to West Palm, she hastily phoned. 'Shelley,' she said, 'don't tell me you're bringing that ugly furniture. You can't take all that crummy furniture all the way to Florida!'

'It's crummy? I like the furniture!'

'Shelley, honey. It's atrocious.'

He called me the following day, dejected. 'What's wrong with the furniture? I *liked* that furniture.'

'If you like it, you should keep it,' I said. 'Dad, it's your house.'

'No,' he said, fatalistic. 'When I redid the kitchen, Seth got mad at me for what I picked. I must have rotten taste. I'm an engineer, I don't have to have good taste.'

'Oh, good taste,' I said. 'Pshaw.'

Sheldon wasn't listening. He said thoughtfully, 'I'll just go to a furniture store and ask the guy what I should buy.'

The result of that procedure was that everything in his house was plush or glass. Every seat was uncomfortably too comfortable like waterbeds. The floppy living-room set looked as if it had fallen asleep sprawled on the floor. Treading across the deep pile carpet through the floaty beige felt like slow motion like a walk on Marshmallow Planet. Then you'd crumple into a colourless too-soft armchair with a quilt ready on one arm, to swaddle yourself to balance the cranked AC.

Here Sheldon arrived and lived without complaint, although he knew one person total (my uncle Sam) in the state of Florida. He had no pastimes and no aims. 'I guess I'll just hang around my bachelor pad. I don't know what people do when they retire. I don't have any hobbies except my dirty movies. I could find a shady lady . . . but I'm too scared of the diseases I'd catch. I'm chicken!'

He went to meetings of the neighbourhood association, whose carping and bickering he deplored, whose bitter decrepit members made him sad. Once in a blue moon he saw Uncle Sam. He had given up on dating, and his life revolved around his daily video rentals and a brand of honey mustard pretzels that was surprisingly low in calories.

The organising principle of his life became his diet. He had to lose eighty pounds to safely undergo hernia surgery; it was a goal. And over the course of a year, he slowly deflated, looking drawn and droopy about the cheeks. His enormous paunch slackened, and he looked somehow cheated, like a little boy who has had a toy snatched from his hands. 'Little pots grow into big cauldrons,' he would intone, as of old. But add, 'I'm getting down to a vat.'

While he was recuperating from the hernia operation, he would need a live-in housekeeper. 'I can't wash dishes or anything,' Sheldon said. 'I'll be in a wheelchair. Oh, boy. I guess it's an excuse to knock off the exercycle. Anyway, I think Uncle Sam knows somebody.'

Housekeeper

'Sandy!'

'Dad! Hi . . . yeah, I've been meaning to call you, but I haven't had a phone. The new place doesn't have a line in.'

'You can use a payphone.'

'That's what I'm doing.'

'Well, that stands to reason.'

We both laughed, I was looking around me at the phone booth as if I wanted to confirm that I was telling the truth. There was a piece of tarnished gum stuck to the payphone instructions panel. Around, the night was raining, drizzle coursing down the phone booth with a continual sliding brightness.

'Well. I'm glad you're still alive,' Sheldon said. Then he added, a little bursting with importance, 'Sandy, I've got news!'

'Good news?'

'Yes! Sandy, I can hardly believe it. The lady Uncle Sam sent to take care of me . . . I've fallen in love with her!'

'Oh.' I caught my breath and I was trying to imagine it. He'd never said anything like that before. It was a tiny Colombian woman with a feather duster. She passed briskly through the living room, Sheldon followed her with his eyes. 'Well, what I mean is, is that good?'

'It's great! I know you're not going to believe this . . . but we were living in the same house, every day. I decided I had to tell her. So I did!'

'And?'

'And she said she had feelings for me, too. Sandy, I'm going to get married!'

Here he got all choked up, he was probably actually tearful. I said sort of shyly, 'I'm so glad for you. After so long.'

'It was worth the wait. Oh, Sandy. She's ...' He swallowed and said in a darker tone, more muted, 'She's a heck of a lot younger. She's thirty-eight.'

'Oh,' I said. I didn't have anything to say about that. I leaned against one wall and put my foot up onto the opposite wall to brace myself. I narrowed my eyes at the rain on the streaming perspex. At last I said, 'So, she's ... twenty-eight years younger?'

'I'm robbing the cradle! She says she doesn't mind. She had a pretty bad time before. Her last husband ... he beat her up, Sandy. He put her in the *hospital*.' His voice caught with disgust. 'He's an – excuse my French – a real ass.'

I gulped and the rain intensified, becoming a noise. I sighed and said, 'Well, then. That makes sense.'

'She loves me,' Sheldon said in a reverent tone, a little muffled with joy.

I was almost crying from some blind sentimentality, the thing that makes you cry at movies. I said, 'Well, that's wonderful. It really is wonderful. So you're getting married?'

'She said she will. I'm a little bit worried she'll come to her senses.' Then he said, making my skin crawl with sympathy, 'Sandy. I'm happy.'

I said, with a tear sneaking out of one eye, blinking at it impatiently, 'God, Dad, God, I'm so glad for you. Give ... what's her name?'

'Diane!'

'... Diane my love.'

Stepmother

They were married in Las Vegas. My brother was best man but I couldn't go. A few months after, though, they visited London. That was when Sheldon emerged from the plane in a wheelchair, terrifying me. He was an old man, a bitter surprise as things are when you have always dreaded them.

The starry-eyed warmth he'd had when he talked about Diane on the phone was gone, but I didn't get to speak to him alone to ask if there was any trouble. In fact, he hardly spoke. He slumped in any seat and stared, morose. He coasted from meal to meal. Diane meanwhile complained, lazily, dispassionately, about the flight, their hotel, the weather, and prices for the five days of their stay.

One afternoon, she took me out to a pub alone. In those years I scarcely drank; the tipsiness from one pint made me anxious like being blindfolded. She told me her friends thought she was crazy to marry a man as old as Shelley, but he made her happy. He was sweet to her. She was good and sick of being treated badly, after her last husband.

I believed her. I was always telling people improbable things – I'm a professional gambler, my real father lives in a castle – so I was biased towards credulity. Plus, there was a dopey, sunny quality to Diane that could be reminiscent of Sheldon in his good moods; after a funny movie, or during a rich dessert. Perhaps they had a bond transcending the obvious. Perhaps every word she said was implausibly true in this most implausible of all possible worlds.

Or the sunniness could be drugs. As the week of their visit wore on, Diane spent increasing amounts of time in a quest through doctors' surgeries, trying to get a prescription for exceptionally strong painkillers. The British doctors wouldn't cooperate, and every night she lay wrapped in a blanket raving about their ignorance, their intransigence, their insensitivity to her extraordinarily savage period pains. So her baseline placidity could be the bleaching out of self from painkillers Diane took that week in handfuls, from her diminishing stock. 'My doctor at home understands. I told them to call him. These schmucks . . .'

Meanwhile Sheldon sat at the hotel table with a book of E–Z crossword puzzles each night. His reading glasses would slip to the end of his nose until he appeared to be straining to focus on the glasses themselves. When Diane called him to witness in her angry laments, he'd focus on the middle distance, seeming disoriented and unsure if he'd heard his name called.

When it wasn't the medication, it was her ex, who was still fighting her in court for her share of the tourist business they'd had in Dauphin Island, Mississippi. 'We'd spend whole days on the boat, showing people where to fish. I worked hard to make that business out of nothing.' Her eyes narrowed as she bore down on her resentment. 'I'm not a vindictive person, only for that man, I am. He chipped away at me. Chip. Chip. Shelley thinks I should get over it . . .'

Sheldon looked up from his E–Z crossword at the middle distance.

'I can't forget it. I can't let go of things like that, the sadism that man showed me. He wants everything I worked to make, but he's kidding himself if he thinks he'll get away with it.'

Sheldon was plying his pencil again.

I said, 'Dad, do you want a tea?'

'What?' He prodded his glasses up the bridge of his nose, and they slipped back down without him seeming to notice.

'Do you want a tea?'

'No, thank you,' he said absently.

'The humiliation that man put me through—'

'Did you hear me, Dad?'

He scratched another two letters in. At last he looked up quizzically at me, a few strands of his hair standing up. 'You're distracting me,' he said in a tone of mock-complaint. 'I'm trying to do my puzzle.'

And for a moment, meeting his eye, I thought I understood. His love affair was over, as a love affair: the worms were out. At his age, he didn't have the energy to get a divorce. And Sheldon had let his life go. He had given up like someone in a moving car letting go of the steering wheel and shutting his eyes.

Seth redux

When the phone call came, I was at Tellex. The supervisor, Mark, a beanpole-type bespectacled man who'd had a story collection out from Faber once but could never complete the follow-up novel, called me to the phone. 'Sandra, it's your brother.'

Seth had never called me in my life. Rising from my chair, I already knew my father was dead.

'Dad died, Sandy. He had a heart attack.'

I had just moved into a new flat. On my way home, I bought a phone. Then I called Seth back from my empty sitting room, sitting on the floor beside my ashtray, feeling white and jarred inside. Making arrangements on the phone, Seth and I were businesslike, discussing Continental versus Virgin, and would orbitz.com get a better price than buying through the airline. But at last Seth said, 'You doing all right, Sandy?' Then I felt cold all over. I remembered I didn't know my brother.

'I guess,' I said. 'Considering. Are you all right?'

'Well, I'm pretty freaking *sad*.' His voice said it was a stupid question. Before I could answer, he said in a rush, 'OK, I love you, Sandy.' Then for the first time in our adult lives I was saying that I loved him, too.

Over the Atlantic, I fell asleep reading some Latin American novel that made my dreams slow and ornate; only at the very end of the flight did Sheldon die and reach up from the hole of night that was swallowing him. I woke with my face to a bank of cloud, my mouth wide open. Then the flight to West Palm Beach from Orlando was beset with wind, the plane made a crashing gesture again and again. I stared down at the tipping water idly wondering if there was life after death. I pressed my thumbs into my eyes and believed in God for a second in which God felt like itching. Then we were touching down, and I walked into the arrivals area, disoriented, and past Seth. He followed behind me laughing.

My brother, for the first time

He was a tall, blonde man with a smudgy Polish bluntness in his features. He dressed as if he worked for the IRS because he did work for the IRS. That was hard to get used to. He was thirty-three and seemed, if anything, older, despite his unlined face. He had an older man's authority. He was nothing like the lumberjack-shirted kid I'd known, or not known; still his goofball humour seemed familiar. It was a deadpan kidding that came from nowhere, from the clear blue sky that was my brother's demeanour. His eyes would shine with pleasure, and winningly he was very easily made to laugh so hard he couldn't breathe. It was more striking because Seth now had perfect manners, an old-school civility he couldn't have learned from our parents. That gave him gravitas, or added the finishing touch to the gravitas that his intelligence gave him. Seth would have made an excellent Senator; born in another family, that would have come naturally to him.

From our parents, he'd learned an aversion to crazy people. Seth had a nervous distaste for neurosis. People should pull themselves together, people shouldn't be whiners, was on the tip of his tongue always. He would spit that out, then look unmanned himself, as if he'd confessed a weakness.

And subtly, like a fine line of wilting at the outermost hem of a petal, Seth was shamed by his depth of emotion. For this reason, he disliked confessions of feeling in others. Of course such confessions are often a stew of the mawkish and the weird; of hypocrisy and exhibitionism. There is no reason to like them. Seth would see them coming far off, though, and change altogether; it was something like an octopus changing shade with feeling. His own confessions were always factual, rushed, almost military in tone. Then the shame came on full force, and my brother seemed frail and sentimental. He would look down at the ground and shuffle his feet. It was what he could not bear.

From the second I got off the plane, Seth behaved as if we had been close always. And I accepted it, in the spirit of Saturnalia which surrounds a funeral: all rules suspended. In that topsy-turvy, the switching on of us as brother and sister, zero to full, passed without comment. He was just my phoenix relative, Seth risen from the ashes of Sheldon, or magically reconstituted from a powder, from a hair. Clap your hands three times when your need is greatest, and I will be there.

I instantly loved him. It was as if he were my brother, and we had grown up in the same house together. It was as if I had always loved him better than anyone in the world.

The crying/laughing phase: days 1–3

Everything was funny, irresistibly. At the supermarket, the family packs of smiley-face cupcakes were transportingly silly, and the frozen diced goat was. An ancient lady halt-ingly crossing the road while putting her lipstick on was priceless, and when we watched *Forrest Gump* that night, every joke in the movie cracked us up. We were staying at Uncle Sam's in his absence, and we laughed until we cried at the Post-It notes he'd left throughout the house. *'This lamp has the switch on the cord. Don't leave it on because the bill goes up.' 'These are the nice spoons, forks, and knives. I don't know why you would use them.' 'Maybe you could leave these Pop Tarts so when I get home, I don't have to shop for Pop Tarts.'*

Also, in the car, in the supermarket, anywhere, I would begin to cry, with a miserable consciousness of public tears as a kind of incontinence. For the most part, everyone – Seth, my aunt Ruth who'd flown in from Chicago, the funeral director – courteously let these tears be a potion of invisibility. Crying conjured an instant solitude. Only once, at the funeral home, Seth touched my shoulder and asked if I was OK, gruffly, like a sergeant bucking up a greenhorn private before a battle.

And at the funeral home, Seth didn't want to see the body but I had to see my father. I went alone into the cheaply carpeted room, absolutely unfurnished like a storeroom. The coffin was white with a plastic finish, dished up on a stage designed to hold bodies after those bodies have cried out, stiffened and seen nothing for the first time. The coffin's top half was open as if to let him breathe. The body looked like a perfect replica of Sheldon, not like Sheldon. I kissed his frozen brow and, cold as water, I got down on my knees and cried from a conditioned reflex triggered when a parent dies.

Really not very much

The day of the funeral we saw Diane. We went to the house, which was still cushy and impersonal, full of the furniture the guy at the furniture store had picked. My brother treated Diane with his unfailing civility, putting everyone at ease. I stood half-crying, silently composing expressions of sympathy to Diane about how she had 'made my father happy in his last years', which I was too embarrassed to say aloud. I said, in an awkward half-voice, 'Nice to see you.'

Diane had put on about a hundred pounds. She was still in primary-schoolteacher clothes, the shapeless colourless hair the same; a pleasant-looking bovine woman. She didn't try seeming sad. Her placid temper even had an air of presentation about it, as if she conceived of it as blameless. Whatever we said or did, she would still be nice and normal, Diane's blasé face said.

Her old friend Beth arrived some minutes after us. I knew Beth's name from the inspirational story of her kicking heroin, going back to school and becoming a highly paid computer programmer in mid-life. It was one of those stories that make you consider becoming a computer programmer. The emaciated and dazed Beth greeted us, slurring her words, and, after a hurried visit to the bathroom, sat down on the deep-pile carpet and passed out. Her face smooshed onto the glass-topped coffee table, she gently snored. Everyone moved and talked around her as if she were not there. When the time came to leave for the funeral, Diane shook her shoulder, and Beth rose and stumbled into the car without fully waking.

Before we left – because we both still smoked then – Seth

and I went out to smoke. I sat on Sheldon's car's front bumper; Seth leaned against the garage door. The warm sun and the smoking were animal pleasures that made sorrow itself feel good. We were chatting about our father's taste in furniture; then about rocker-recliners as a class, in a satiric vein. 'Mmm, Naugahyde,' Seth said, for instance, and that alone was enough to make us laugh that day. Then Seth fell silent and began to regard the toes of his dress shoes in a constrained way I would come to recognise. At last he said, 'You know, Sandy . . . Dad didn't leave us very much.'

I baulked. I looked at the crown of my brother's head, that was greying in an anomalous patch on one side. The grey spot seemed like an expression of his personality, something Seth had put on to cheer the troops. The inheritance – which I had often speculated about, guiltily imagining the flat I'd buy – had stopped meaning anything the instant my father died. Now I pondered the coming years of typing, the chronic housing problems, the dentist issue. The animal pleasure of smoking made this seem a comfortable misery, like a fond but sexless marriage. 'Well, that's OK,' I said with the fondness in my voice. 'I mean, he did remarry. That's what you'd expect.'

'No, I mean.' Seth cleared his throat. '*Really* not very much.' Then he shrugged and he was smoking, looking at me with a queasiness that referred to something unsaid.

I squinted at him. I was smoking and my heart was going in and out. It was like a balloon inflating and deflating into sharp colour. I couldn't ask what he meant. I couldn't: it was something to do with Sheldon complaining, with heartfelt injustice, that I only called when I wanted money. He would say it whenever I wanted money, as a subtle argument against my deserving money. Now it seemed more vital than ever to win that argument, as if I could finally prove I was his daughter.

I squinted up the street at the regular series of box houses silhouetted against the sun-bleached blue. A rank of spindly palm trees stood a little bowed, discouraged, their few leaves seeming like the issue of a particular, miserly creation. There was no wind, nothing stirred: the place stood blankly in a pesticide silence. I said with that blankness, 'That's OK.'

Seth made a face and looked at his feet more fiercely. Then he dropped his cigarette and rubbed it out with the toe of his shoe. 'I hope so.'

The funeral took place in that storeroom-like space where I had viewed my father's corpse. The room was now adorned with metal folding chairs and a podium on wheels. The carpet had been tacked down inexpertly so it rolled in gray billows. There were no windows, and one ceiling tile was missing. Cables from the sound system ran across the stage behind the coffin.

No one came but a handful of Diane's friends. There was a biker in a leather vest; there was a ponytailed man called 'Coon'. The friends were either fat or skeletal. Dull-eyed relics of the trash South, they sat slumped through the service. They were a graphic reminder of Diane's last occupation, small-town bartender.

The skinny red-haired rabbi wore a determined grin, and seemed a little underprepared, like a public defender on a chickenshit criminal case. He delivered rote nonsense about Sheldon being a man everybody held dear, loved by his colleagues, friends and family, to an audience of eight. Afterwards, Diane's friends shuffled around Diane, talking to her in an undertone. None of them talked to us.

The circumstances

Sheldon had gone to the doctor complaining of shortness of breath – a concern because of the heart attack he'd had some fifteen years before. The doctor could find nothing, and my father was sent home. The next day he was found dead in his armchair, foam coming out of his mouth, no turning back. The ambulance was called and a death certificate issued. Cause of death: cardiac arrest. He was sixty-six years old.

The sheriff issuing the death certificate called Sheldon's doctor's office and left a message.

Later that day, the doctor's office called. Apparently they hadn't heard the message about my father's death. They left a voicemail saying there was something strange in the blood work; could Mr Newman come in? Although we phoned repeatedly, that was the last we ever heard from Sheldon's doctor.

We never discovered what, if anything, was strange about our father's blood. Diane didn't want an autopsy. That was the decision of the wife under Florida law. Although my brother offered to pay, she said the carving up of the body would be traumatic. My father was cremated three days after I arrived in West Palm Beach.

In his will, Sheldon left $10,000 to my brother and $5,000 to me. There was no explanation given for the disparity. The remainder of his money, along with his house and his possessions, he left to his wife of one year, Diane.

Ritual

Seth and I spent our last day in Florida looking through my father's papers. We knew, because Sheldon had told us, that he'd had a life insurance policy for $200,000 with Seth and me as beneficiaries. Neither of us, however, had any documentation. We didn't even know what company held the policy. Unless we found the papers, we were reduced to hoping someone at the insurance company read Sheldon's funeral notice and was motivated by disinterested altruism to pay out on the policy.

When we went to the house, Diane was cordial, casual, waving at us to do whatever as she drifted back to the TV. With the TV's soothing voice in the background, Seth and I dragged several plastic crates of papers, folders, albums, out into the middle of the living-room carpet. We sat cross-legged on the floor to sort.

Our whole family's paperwork was there, moved wholesale from Massachusetts because my father didn't want to go through it. Old telephone bills were wedged in between the pages of company newsletters. I found Sheldon's passport circa 1968, and movie tickets to *Star Wars* from a decade later. My third grade report card was mashed into an accordioned wad with a Chinese take-out menu. The repetitive nature of the task was calming. Like all work in the wake of a death, it felt like shoring up the barricades against any future mortality.

In a canvas bag with a patchwork quilt print, I found my diary from the year of Louise's death, the only year I kept a diary. Typed on loose paper in that fifties Smith Corona typeface, it distracted me for some time while my brother flipped mechanically through bank statements. I had been a tiresome child, to judge by the diary. The style was whiny girlspeak, and the content was pedantic exegesis of my every mood. The diary kept close track of my evolving opinion of my sex appeal compared with other girls. Reading it, I began to feel a prickly misogyny. Oddly, I remembered everything differently from how my thirteen-year-old self recorded it. I couldn't help feeling I was right and this brattish kid was wrong. The entry on the day of my mother's death was particularly heavy with narcissistic musings, and I finally pulled the diary out and stowed it in my satchel to deal with later in privacy. I flipped through a couple of bills, relieved. Then I found my mother's suicide note.

Dear Shelley,

I know this is wrong, but I can't stand to live with what I've done to you and the kids. I hope someday you'll forgive me and understand that I love you and Sandy and Seth very much. By the time you read this ...

I don't know which suicide it was from. I had never seen the note before. The time she died, she left no note, as far as I know. The fact of it was startling, but the content was generic. By the time I got to the end, my attention was flagging. I didn't recognise Louise in it. It was like a suicide note copied out of Emily Post.

I sat for a long time, stroking the paper with my fingertips, trying to get it to yield some taste of my mother's personality. Her hands had touched this paper. She would have been devastated then. There should be a deposit of tragic emotion in the note, at least a wistful trace or ghost. Of course, I felt nothing.

*   *   *

When Seth and I took a smoke break, I mentioned the suicide note without thinking.

He shrugged and seemed to clench with unhappiness. He said, 'Well, that's freakin' cheerful. This all sucks.' He looked at his watch. 'We're not going to get through it, either. I think I'm going to take the papers back to Mass. If you want, you should come. Come for a couple weeks.'

'Yeah, OK,' I said, stunned. Then I said, to act like staying with Seth was no big deal, 'I'll have to get back reasonably soon, for work.'

'Sure.' Seth shrugged. 'I'll pay for the ticket. I know you don't have much money.'

'Thanks,' I said. Then I cleared my throat and said, 'Hey, have you ever tried quitting smoking?'

'Yeah, I've tried,' Seth said. 'They're going to have to pry this cigarette from my cold, dead hand. Naw, I'll try again, I don't know.'

Both of us were silent a moment; as if we were waiting for the words *cold, dead* to dissipate in the air. I began to ponder how my friend Clive, a cabinetmaker by profession, once said he wanted to start a business building coffin wardrobes. They would range from simple boxes to ornate inlaid sarcophagi (Clive had a knack for fine carving) and would be provided with a rail inside to hang clothes. The rail would fit into a housing and be easily removable in case of death. Then the person would replace the shirts and be set for handy burial.

The coffin wardrobe would be a memento mori in your bedroom, politely waiting for you while you made love, fell into your restless sleep, woke up with a start to remember that your father was dead. And it occurred to me then that the body was a coffin. We were going to be buried in these arms, legs, and torsos. We were walking around and making love, falling into our restless sleep and smoking in the clingy West Palm pinkish humidity in our coffins. I looked at Seth, his features sensitive in a way that did not suit him, and wanted him never to think of these things. Seth wasn't going to die. He didn't have a morbid streak. He would never be ready to die, that was for people like me and Clive.

Seth sighed and I blurted to shed the cold, dead mood, 'I found my diary from when I was thirteen. I was an incredibly annoying kid.' I looked down, suddenly nervous. I'd forgotten Seth knew me at that age. I'd forgotten that anyone knew me at that age.

'Awww,' Seth said, rousing himself. 'Everyone's an asshole at thirteen. For Christ's sake, that's when the asshole hormones get you. Don't sweat that.'

'No, I think I was worse.'

'Yeah, you were an asshole,' Seth said loudly. 'I'm an asshole, everybody's an asshole.'

I laughed thinly, squeaky. We tossed our cigarettes down in a unison of feeling, I'm not sure what concentrated feeling. Without looking at each other, we went back in. The screen door seemed to thinly laugh in closing: Diane started and woke to look at us dreamily from her recliner. By the time we had settled behind our crates, she was nodding again, one hand clutching the remote control to her stomach like a favourite doll. She was watching a talk show on which Tom Hanks was being interviewed about an upcoming movie.

'That the character has these unfulfilled facets, exactly,' Hanks was saying. 'And there comes a point where he'll do anything to satisfy them, even if he loses his son.' Diane's eyelids were almost shut, and her mouth had drifted open. One chubby whitish hand twitched in the first throes of sleep. She was sitting in the chair where my father had died.

That's taking it too far, that's pathological, just say things

On the flight to Massachusetts I still didn't know Seth had a girlfriend. He let it slip in dribs and drabs. First he mentioned that a friend would be picking us up. Then, as the flight was landing, I gleaned that this friend lived with Seth. As we approached the baggage claim, the friend turned female, but the word 'friend' still left me wondering. It was only when we came out and Seth saw Vita that I knew.

My brother was deeply in love. I think I blushed with surprise. Vita had come forth beaming and flung her arms around him. She was hugging him one way, then another and kissing him on the lips. Seth stood there mortified and shining, kind of, with his love.

He said, 'OK, already! OK! Vita, you're nuts,' all choked up, laughing.

Then she abandoned him and hugged me for good measure. She said, a little scrambling to say it so fast in her Latvian accent, 'Sandy, it's good to meet you! I'm so glad I meet one of Seth's family. He won't tell anything about you, ever, it's driving me really crazy!'

The perfect girlfriend

Vita was *brevis* of course (five foot one), chubby, button-nosed, had long plenteous flaxen hair and an open-heartedness that stumped you. Seth and I both laughed at almost anything Vita said. She'd dimpled, and you didn't have defences left, you had to admire the surefooted way she chose the happy path. Maybe it was the lack of adult guile that made it funny. It was her suburban house and Daisy the Labrador pelting through the big backyard, it was her baggy sweatshirts and her beatific humour, her blithe concept of life's basics – pizza, haunted houses, dog toys. She'd brought her younger sister over from Latvia, and they lived in the house together as if there had never been discord in the world. Vita was only twenty-four years old.

In Latvia, she had studied to make and restore stained glass. While she went to school, she was living with Riga cousins who hated her. She took up room, ate food, and where Vita was concerned the mother of the family was all criticism, railing and eye-rolling. After Vita graduated, worse, she couldn't find work. 'Everybody was angry, everybody shouting at me. My parents, my cousins. One is shouting on the phone, at the same time the other one is shouting to my face, it's terrible,' Vita told me laughingly. Then, through an émigré uncle, she got the offer of a job in America.

She came to Massachusetts and stayed with the aged uncle, a more light-hearted man who immediately took to her. They shared a sense of humour. They used to drink beer together and watch *Letterman*. She mowed the lawn and cooked, and she'd do handy work around the house he couldn't do with his arthritis. Vita's job was in a factory, embroidering names on work shirts, mottos on T-shirts. She saved her money and started to go to college for graphic design.

One year later, the uncle died. He left his house to Vita. The cousins fumed in vain.

'They think I stole his money,' Vita said and laughed, radiating happiness. 'They asked me to give the house back, but I said no.'

'Screw them,' Seth said. 'Those jerks should have treated you better.'

Vita shrugged and said, 'What I'm going to do, without a house?'

At dinner that night, after she'd checked that Seth was not depressed four times ('Honestly, Vita. I wouldn't lie to you.') she suddenly turned to me and asked, 'Sandy, how did your mother die?'

'God, Vita!' said Seth. 'Give her a chance—'

I was already laughing. I said, in the wrong way, light-hearted, 'Well, she killed herself.'

'That's it!' said Vita. ''Cause Seth won't tell me. I knew it's something.'

'What does it matter, Vita?' Seth said. 'What's the difference?'

'A lot of difference,' Vita said good-naturedly. 'And how does she kill herself?'

I said, 'Well, pills.'

'Now, you see?' Vita said. 'Why it's bad to know this, I don't know.'

'But why do you want to know?' Seth said. 'It doesn't change anything. You're never going to meet her.'

'Sandy knows why,' said Vita confidently. Then she said, with a cherishing tone, as if it were a wonderful gift she was turning over in her hand, 'Pills!'

Life after death

She put me in the spare room, a room that smelled like the bedrooms of my childhood: forest floor and fabric softener. There was a white teddy bear sitting tilted on top of the dresser my brother had had in our childhood home. The bear looked quizzical, one paw propped against my father's rubber Oliver Hardy figurine. I lay with the sheet up to my nose, looking at the vinyl shades on the windows that were the same kind I'd had in my bedroom as a child. I lay there trying to understand my father's death, as if, with the requisite effort, I could coax my own death from my memory.

When I die in a dream, I feel my throat constrict and the world dims, numbs headlong and I know I'm about to die. I realise it's for real this time. I wonder if there's anything after death, whether a bead of consciousness will slip intact from my dead body. Blackness dawns and I wake up.

The dream death replayed in my mind. It was the thought of my father's fear I couldn't stand. He was afraid and then it didn't stop happening.

He had sat doing crosswords, and his mussed grey hair, his apathy, gave the London hotel room a hospice's workaday despair. Diane ranting in her chair was poison. Only family can speak out in such a case. I had thought, he is drifting into death. But I hadn't had that bone dread prompting rescue, that blood zeal I supposed a non-adopted child would have. And in the months that followed, I had been preoccupied, going behind his back with a Johnny-come-lately father (who flashed in my mind as glad and

invulnerable, in his white stronghold in the optimistic West
– here the vision stopped in a cramp of guilt).

And Vita's house was in our home town, Chelmsford, a
fact that was embroiled somehow unhappily with the fact
that Seth had stayed close to my father, and with whatever
had happened in West Palm Beach.

Prenup

In the prenuptial agreement, it was stipulated that if Diane and Sheldon divorced after one year, she would get 1 per cent of his assets. If they divorced after two years, she got 3 per cent. After three years, 5 per cent. At fifteen years, it hit 50 per cent, and stopped. These were clearly provisions preventing her from divorcing Sheldon rapidly and seeking half his assets.

As long as they stayed married, however, all their property was held in common. In the case of his death, she inherited everything. Sheldon did not even have the right to bequeath any money away from Diane without her written agreement. The will my father had left was superceded by this prenup. Of course he couldn't have known that because he'd taken the trouble and expense to make the will.

On the phone, Diane told Seth in her sleepy blunt manner that she'd decided not to give him the $10,000 my father had mentioned in his will. 'Shelly loaned you money two years ago to start a law office. So I decided to forgive you that loan in lieu of the money.' As far as my money went, 'I think I'll give Sandy her $5,000 in a year.' She offered no reason for the delay.

Every day I looked through papers while Seth was at work. He came home and looked through papers. We had started by looking for insurance documents, but it grew into an inquest into my father's marriage. When I found vacation photos I put them aside for Seth. There was a handwritten, unfinished letter in which my father – naively, gushingly – told Diane he sometimes thought she was more mature than he was, because she'd been through so much. There was a bank statement showing that $200,000 had been moved from his personal account into their joint account ten days before his death, that I seized on and presented to Seth with the thrill of a point scored for our team.

I phoned Sheldon's doctor in West Palm every morning and left messages. The doctor never returned my calls, and sometimes I got frantic as if there was still time left to save Sheldon's life. On his lunch hour, Seth was phoning Florida probate lawyers, looking for someone to contest the will.

One evening, on a smoke break in Vita's garage, Seth ventured, 'Yeah, you just have to wonder.' He baulked and looked down at his feet intently. 'Whether she had anything to do with it.'

I caught my breath. I looked at the door to the house, even though Vita wasn't home. We were smoking too fast.

'But I guess Dad had a heart attack before,' I said.

'Yeah. It just looks so freakin' bad.' Seth shrugged. He'd begun to shift his feet uncomfortably, looking at them in a way that was almost demure. He looked like a hick kid out of his depth in the big city.

I said, my voice fetching up on this, 'No, I know it seems crazy, it's like something from a movie, to suspect she might have *murdered him.*' Then the words 'murdered him' seemed to boom around the garage, sounding surreal, absurd. It was like my parleys as a child with Sandra Jill Cameron, when we had to conceal from the world that we could see tiny animals that lived on sticks.

We had no rational reason to imagine Diane killed my father. Sheldon's older brother and sister had both died in their sixties. His was not a long-lived family. Sheldon was not a healthy man. He'd had a heart attack before, and he was very overweight, and it was overdue. But Seth and I were losing our minds from the tawdry grind of it, the bargain-basement trophy widow violating our clean grief. If she had killed him, we would have a way to punish Diane for having married our father.

No Florida probate lawyer would touch it. There was no reason to think that Sheldon was under duress or senile, the only reasons a will could be contested. We couldn't pay up front. There was no chance of winning. There wasn't sufficient evidence to convince a DA to start criminal proceedings, either. It was a brick wall.

I went back to London. I was back at Tellex.

A few months after these events, I called Diane. My excuse to myself was the $5,000. Really it was a scab-picking impulse; what makes you poke a bruise to make sure it still hurts.

I left a message on her answering machine, which still used the name Diane Newman. Of course she never returned my call. When I tried back two months later, the phone was answered by a privacy gadget that announced, 'You have reached a number with Call Director.' Call Director wouldn't take a message unless the caller's number was in the gadget's vetted list. Finally, six months later, I phoned one last time, with no expectation. Call Director was gone. But the message said, 'You have reached Diane and Raoul.'

My brother and I kept in contact, exactly as if we had always been good friends. Gradually my father and the money he'd left faded from our talks. At last one day, when I mentioned Diane, Seth said abruptly, 'Sandy. I think it's time to forget about that.'

For a second I was scrambling for a way to not have said it.

Seth said, in a tone of cutting through my sentimental illusions, 'You got to think about what Dad was thinking when he signed that prenup.'

'Sure,' I said. 'I mean, I guess.'

'He signed that of his own free will. Yeah, he could have taken care of us.' Then Seth's voice stopped dead.

'Maybe he—'

'I'm only saying.'

I was tongue-tied for a minute, remembering suddenly my birth father, and the Strugatsky brothers novel I'd been reading when I got his letter. The alien struggles to be reunited with the only artefact from his planet. If he can reach it, something will happen – the one vital thing will happen. It's a story, like so many stories, about a child's quest for his real father. And I realised Seth and I were brother and sister divided by the fact that only he was orphaned. In that moment of useless empathy, my back-up parents seemed like the spoils of unnatural crime. I thought, I have retrieved my object, but Seth hasn't – and was sick on the hubris that makes you long to help other people, while they wrack their brains for a way of helping you.

Then he cleared his throat and said casually, 'So, I guess I'm moving to Washington in April, not in March. So if you wanted to visit . . .'

11

Happy Ending

The love of my life

at the time my happy ending happened was a big ex-felon of an ex-smack addict, scarred from head to toe; a pussycat really as people say. When we met, Robert Burrows had only been off heroin three months. He was still living in rehab; puffy and pale from detox, in that generalised shame phase where he only felt right expiating or confessing.

We met at a holiday shelter for the homeless: Crisis Open Christmas. It was in a donated warehouse space that transformed in minutes when the homeless arrived into a city of the damned of smells and rags and sobs and trances of rage. Both Rob and I did seven overnights, a week stitched together from bone-tired little hours. The volunteers and homeless increasingly resembled each other, meeting in a general semi-dereliction morning seven. Rob and I spent hours paired on fire watch, whispering stories at the edge of a muttering city block of mattresses, intimate with stink and tired and dark.

In our first conversation, Rob confessed he was an addict in recovery. When I asked what drug, he said in an undertone, 'Heroin, really.' Then he noticed himself soft-pedalling, and laughed with great good cheer. 'Hark at me!' he said weakly. 'As if there were any question! Heroin *definitely*. Heroin without one iota of doubt!'

Rob was a cockney guttersnipe (his word for himself) whose one job ever had been street-sweeping for Hackney Council. Even as a boy, he'd wanted to be a junkie, like his rock-star heroes, like (like legions of addicts of about Rob's age) Keith Richards. He was trying to score before anyone would sell drugs to him, he was only a child. Perseverance paid. He left school at thirteen; at fourteen his parents threw him out. By then, he had the habit of his dreams, and belonged in the street with the other junkies, sleeping in subway tunnels and doorways.

Twenty-eight years passed.

They were years of wards and cells and squats and rehabs, where he was ever injecting some crushed pain pill that wasn't designed to be injected. The pills left residue in his veins, and gave him diseases of the aged. He had sores on his feet that wouldn't heal, deep vein thrombosis. His arms, legs and groin were covered in scars and sores; no major vein was whole; his hands were red and swollen. He was skeletal and walked on crutches for years at a time in youth.

Like most reformed characters, he could be vain about how low he'd sunk. He'd nearly died, he'd brag. For years he loitered on the line between life and death. Once he died and got brought back, though he didn't see any heavens or hells. He was on a first-name basis with the ambulance drivers and EMTs throughout the East End, and there was a month he overdosed so many times that he had more hospital admissions than there were days in that month. He would be released, score, sit on a doorstep, and take all the drugs at once, waking up hours later in the same ward to the same war-weary nurse. Repeat.

One paranoid year he wouldn't leave the house without a sharpened stick; he harboured a dark conviction that London was the haunt of vampires. He'd been in psych wards where the men were given paper clothes to prevent escapes, and cell blocks where they were given rubber clothes to save on laundry. One rehab specialised in shame techniques, making the men wear clown make-up or spend twelve hours in front of a mirror, or both at once.

Once he'd been in a chemist's, stoned to the level of reptile intelligence, and discovered a tower of talismans in such mesmerising colours that he began to greedily scoop them (Maybelline eyeshadows) into his pockets, when the cops arrived. It was that stuff, slobbering stupid crimes, too high to know and shooting up on the cop-shop stairs or caught on a doctor's doorstep fishing through the letter slot with a coat hanger trying to snag the doctor's bag for the prescription pad.

The things that caused him shame weren't those, but things like robbing his mother's neighbours; or the impromptu cavity searches of passed-out junkie girls, looking for their stash. Once Rob caught a friend trying to steal his drugs and beat his face in with a clay spade. The horror-movie image of the torn face with teeth gone and the nose shorn half off was Rob's flashback, it never quit tormenting him. He met that man in prison later, disfigured, face lopsided and trenched with scars, but the bloke said no worries, he would have done the same. Rob beat up one dealer in front of the man's whole family, the children screaming, the wife begging him to leave off. That man had cheated him of £10. Rob would return to these points again and again, and they would always be the same, no detail of them would alter no matter how much Rob changed. It was a disfigured face that would not right itself; who cared whether it said it forgave you?

And he was still puzzled by, unreconciled to, all the death he'd seen; his personal holocaust of overdosing, suiciding, murdered friends left a mark on him, as if a god had blundered through and left nothing quite right, ever again. It wasn't grief – death was too commonplace for grief – it was an aching wonder at the scale. 'She's dead, now, and the bloke she was with is dead. And the girl I lived with then is dead. I'm the sole survivor, Miss N!' He'd laugh, but shake his head, and tack on in a confidential undertone, 'Horrible, actually. It scares the shit out of me, actually.'

Off drugs, in weeks he grew to a hearty ox of a man with crime still written all over him in scars and homemade blue tattoos. He'd say, 'I used to bang up heroin on the train, I was never ashamed of nothing then. Now I'm ashamed of everything. I'm shit-scared of everything. I'm a discombobulated ball of shame and fear!' Laughing merrily, he would add, 'Don't laugh, this is deadly serious!'

Indestructible, Rob had the substantial presence of an oak or an ogre maybe. His sincerity was oaken too. He was every Simpleton from a fairy tale who shows outrageous wisdom, slays the dragon, saves the town, by not understanding that anyone could have baulked, that anyone could have acted on an unworthy thought. Selfishness was what people did when they were using, Rob thought. Now that he was clean, he was shut of all that fucking nightmare. And I fell in love with Rob at least partly because of the figure I cut, or the story I was telling, by taking the ogre in – who needed me, who could never, he said, have stayed off drugs without me. Meanwhile Rob adored me like that imaginary beast, that figment would. He loved me more than anyone deserves to be loved. He would say to me out of nowhere, 'Totally smitten,' all transfixed and lost. Or he'd say, 'I would take a bullet for you, Miss N,' in rash romantic foolery. But it was as good as true; I would have too. I loved him so much it made every second of those years pink, or made them tipsy, whatever the adjective is. It was an adjective that could have turned into a snowy bird and flown away to tell the emperor's fortune. That love changed me into a different person with different bones and skin. It changed me into the person I could have been.

At the end, superstitious villagers chase the monster onto the Arctic ice. The fabulous bird escapes through the Emperor's folly, and love's empire falls to ruin. There are rules to storybook loves. Only real-world loves, satisfied with shared interests and shared meals – that small beer – endure.

While it lasts: my five best years

Our flat was in a council estate in Vauxhall. The building was brick, sedate, four storeys: identical buildings spread in all directions for blocks and blocks. Most of the people were black working class. In Vauxhall, there was a spate of gun murders at that time, but the poverty was generally slipshod and pitiful, not cut-throat.

Rob was always in a war with the upstairs neighbour Cassie over noise. She liked her music to tremble in the concrete walls. Her ordinary speaking voice was a bray that shook the lamps, compared with which her toddler's scream was faint, a scratching nothing. She had floor-pounding, shrieking sex with her fat white skinhead boyfriend, and rows of which we'd hear just her side: 'Don't you tell me! – Fuck that! – Well, *this* black cunt had your child!' At last he was chucked out, to be replaced weeks later by a new fat skinhead, this one carrot-haired and peacable.

She was a big soppy girl very easily moved to tears and tempers, with a numerous West Indian and white family who often gathered to drink beer on her balcony, making less noise in the aggregate than she did alone. Rob went up to yell about the noise so many times that Cassie and he became fast friends. She was a scrub nurse, and thrilled Rob with the information that the doctors cranked Led Zeppelin during surgery.

Below us lived a retired white concert pianist who spoke in a whisper, in which you could make out the fading intonations of gay voice. He had forty-odd cats that trotted in and out of his open door and lay strewn about the parking lot. They made our part of the building stink. The pianist was convinced that the neighbourhood was rife with crime, and confided in us his delusion that Cassie was running a brothel. He heard sex noises, and saw men and white girls coming in and out. All the black kids were drug runners in his frightened opinion, and no reassurances helped. He would limp off shaking his head at our naivety.

Most of the people in the block were African; private people, a little mistrustful. Our window into our neighbours' world was through their kids, who played in the parking lot all day, and followed us upstairs sometimes with left-field childish questions: 'Is that bicycle fast? Do you like my hair? Do you have a middle name?' A couple of times I brought them into the flat with me. They were smitten with the manual typewriter, which to them was an antique computer. When they left, they all went off with token trophies: a button, a matchbox car, a ponytail holder, souvenirs from an age when someone else's flat is a foreign country.

I was so happy in that council block I possibly never understood it; all seemed right. Rob and I were under the spell of a hopeful worthiness. We were trying to begin our lives, too late, and being overworked became a principle. After work, we worked. I would seldom even read a novel because it served no useful purpose. I wrote at night, but also painted all our walls. All meals must be from scratch. Riding my bike in all weathers, working all hours, was to pare myself down somehow until I could see the kernel. And I was trying to be a good person, self-consciously, painstakingly, because it was what I could have.

At first, Rob volunteered full-time at a detox. Nights, he studied for a counselling certificate, went to NA meetings, fought the paperwork battles ex-prisoners and dole recipients are ever mired in. When the certificate was earned, he got a paid job at a homeless shelter in Vauxhall. Then he was respectable: 'Upstanding member of society, Sans!'

Meanwhile, I worked at Tellex, then at temp jobs, then at Tellex. I'd begun what would become my first published novel. When I wasn't applying for jobs, I applied for master's programmes in creative writing – at first in the US, because the only British programme then was the prestigious University of East Anglia course. I assumed they would not have me; no such seat of privilege could want me. When Rob's application for an American visa was turned down, though, for his drug offences, I applied there in a last-ditch effort and got in.

I used to go running at night, and I could start at my doorstep and in five minutes be on the Thames embankment going along the river where Big Ben and the Houses of Parliament would be lit up and also reflected into the grey Thames like up-and-down fairyland. It was when the London Eye was under construction, and the ferris wheel was hung out flat over the river. The embankment was still deserted at night. And I remember those years, the final, peaceful, poverty years, as if they were a solitude; as if I ran along the river through an evacuated London. The fairy lights on Westminster and wavering lights in the water below were a Fata Morgana. The only other person in the city was Rob.

Our wedding was at an evangelical church in Brixton. The church was a little two-storey house with a green neon cross like a French pharmacy. The reverend was coincidentally American, and had worked for NASA before discovering Jesus and entering the ministry. He was the only white man in his congregation, a beefy folksy affable man, who made himself well-liked universally, via schmaltz, as some Americans can.

For me, the wedding was characterised by being terrified by bliss, blissed out by fear, a downward plunge of the roller coaster. Screaming and grinning at once, that rabbit-in-the-headlights joy, while friends all snapped our pictures. The service itself was marked by unabashed sentimentality. The audience were mostly Rob's Narcotics Anonymous friends, long-term junkies now detoxed, rehabbed, and in that shame phase; hyper-sensitive, earnest. The reverend gave a rain-of-schmaltz speech like an American politician's, with a forced metaphor meant to inspire (marriage = super-glue). The whole audience was teary-eyed, it became a funny story after, all those addicts primed by NA to think in miracles blubbered. It was like the concluding wedding scene of an unrealistic chick-flick.

My real parents gave me away. I had asked Seth to do it, but he didn't come. It was an awkward time at work, he said, it was hard to get time off in June. I felt awkward, a little repentant: I had meant it to establish him as my main relative, in case he felt usurped by the biological family. I also wanted them all to meet. Now that aim felt tactless, borderline transgressive. The two logically contradictory families should not be in the same room: it was as if I were irresponsibly coaxing a time traveller to meet himself.

My good friend Helen, who had been a witness at my wedding to Amos, was a witness at this one, too. Helen is a born-again bourgeoise, who had been a speed freak young in the London clubs before realising that she hated noise and crowds. What she liked was a glass of red in a well-kept garden, she liked international travel and good conversation. She had known me, Will, and Amos since for ever. Helen has a freakish gentle wit but brooks no nonsense; in these years I was self-conscious with her. I felt she must see marrying Rob as an arrant break with reason, though she was too kind and British to say anything but that she liked him.

And Will was there with his best girlfriend of all, Elisa. Elisa had a softness in her manner that made her lovely face seem timeless; she was sensitive, brainy, quiet. It was Elisa who taught us a ready resource to be instantly happy. Stand facing someone else. Each party should place his/her hands on the other party's shoulders. Then the two jump up and down in unison. Sadness flies.

Helen, Will, Elisa, and I stood together a while at the tail end of the festivities, watching the sun set over lumpish Brixton. A pool of rosy light on the skin of a parking lot looked lacy; a balding tree held its few hands up as if to show it was hiding nothing. In the distance, a spilled trash bin looked like a cornucopia. The scene's ugliness seemed humble: beauty of soul. And we talked about Tony Blair's teeth and the last Tube strike, etc., safe bland topics. At last Will and Elisa turned to go. As we watched them walk away, Will loose-kneed with the Scotch he'd been sipping from a flask throughout, Helen said, *sotto voce*, 'She won't last.'

More happy ending

All creative writing programmes are centred around workshops. In a fiction workshop, a student will submit twenty-odd pages of writing, and at the next class everyone discusses the work. Discussion means criticism, and the aim of a workshop is to work out the kinks in a novel, a short-story collection, one's writing practice overall, and come out at the end as a professional with a saleable book.

But every person approaching a writing workshop for the first time has the secret expectation that her work will defy criticism. Her book is already a masterpiece, and she will instantly be hailed as a rising star. The famous writer leading the workshop will single her out for praise, and she will be offered referrals to agents and editors. The atmosphere will be like a festival, all the other writers delighted to award the laurels to her, the astonishing talent who stands head and shoulders above.

That was what happened to me.

At my entrance interview for the University of East Anglia, the head of the programme, Andrew Motion, told me immediately that I was already accepted, blurting the news as if he couldn't wait to say how much he valued my writing. Then he raved about my fiction while my face burned and I didn't understand. It was as if good fortune was tripping over itself in its rush to fall into my lap, it was gratuitous kindness from the universe and Mr Motion personally. I could have cried, though I satisfied myself with being very dizzy and laughing too much as we talked about God knows what for our ten minutes. I think it was Dickens.

W. G. Sebald led my first workshop – a courtly man with

an introspective gravitas, mild, and giving the impression of wisdom actually. The day the beginning of my novel was considered, Sebald started discussion with, 'I don't know what we can say about this, except that it is very good.' Then, all around the room, the students were nodding and smiling at me like fond parents. It was a scene that could have been written by my ego, surreal the way it is when a lover says, 'I love you,' the first time, unwittingly acting the role your fantasies wrote for them in ever so many sleepless nights. It was (if it had not been me) sickening.

So I became one of the favourites of that year. I was a messy starveling thing, still dressed in cheap old clothes and scared to meet strangers' eyes, I was like an anaemic child. Some other students already had book deals; many had come from jobs in publishing, theatre, the BBC. It was easy, I guess, to make me the underdog genius. My work was experimental, uncommercial, and I was a girl. It probably seemed a badge of integrity to exalt me over e.g. the student whose first novel had made him (so said gossip) half a million with the foreign rights. I was, in short, a fad.

I began to be conscious of my status. Trivial acts of thoughtfulness from me counted now, were thoughtfulness and not just blather. I praised someone, and the person reacted with startling, heartfelt gratitude that humbled me and made the world feel gracious. There is no luxury like the power to give. Low-status people can't be kind, that way – their kindness is missed in the rush past them, or treated as minimal dues. It can be, at worst, impertinent. 'You look beautiful,' said the executive; 'You look beautiful,' said the homeless man: two different things.

Andrew Motion gave me referrals to agents, but it was a new friend, Millie, who gave me the introduction to the agent I still have today, Victoria Hobbs. Victoria was an old friend of Millie, though they were no longer on speaking terms. They'd parted after some bad moment when Victoria was hungover and Millie too forcefully insisted she ought to eat strawberries for the vitamin C. Perhaps it was cantaloupe. The whole dispute was one of those things whose significance only the principals grasp; it was the *way* she did it, and the *history*. Victoria loved my book, was the point, and I had that meeting in her office where she talked about how much. It was having a cup of coffee with someone about my age; and it was the fulfilment of my life's work. So many triumphs are this quiet. Likewise, the scene in which I learned my book had been accepted for publication was a brief phone call, and changed everything about my life.

The money from the sale bought me out of the day job. Without the endless rote work, I was a different person. My insomnia vanished; back pain that I'd had for a decade vanished. For the first time, I loved people. I was outgoing suddenly, meeting all the people I'd been too ashamed to know before. Strangers were interested in me; it wasn't like being a typist. My old friends said, 'No one deserves it more than you,' with passion, nearly anger, with a catch in their voices.

The book (*The Only Good Thing Anyone Has Ever Done*) was published to critical acclaim. I appeared on radio, talking about it; I was interviewed for newspapers. People warmed to that odd book, it was a heartfelt shy book, somehow. It was pretty, and geeky, it was like a novel that was frightened of people and trying to put on a brave face. It was shortlisted for the *Guardian* First Book Award; in America, it sold to HarperCollins. My friends all liked it, and their friends did. Friends of friends would phone to say they'd loved my book. Not a cloud in the sky! I have good news that I'm delighted to give you, because no one deserves it more!

I wrote another novel and co-authored a writing manual. Universities gave me teaching posts. Hard work bred success in the way it had been fabled to do, even though I had already seen through that deceitful fable. I bought whole meals in restaurants now, not just the soup of the day. I no longer blushed at attending a yoga class; I would buy clothes at the Gap. I made new, different, friends; people who belonged to gyms and cooked from cookbooks, who had taken drugs recreationally, in college. I'd become one of the fortunate people I once resented.

And it didn't seem to be a problem in those days – it was even a relief from the stress of that sudden visibility – that the only person I knew who never read my book was Rob.

12

The Happy Ending Ending

About the time we were married, Rob began to lose his temper. Mundane disagreements – whether to get a dog, when to go on vacation – sent him to a zenith of anger. My mess drove him mad. Sometimes this was real slovenliness – towels and clothes on the floor, strewn papers, dirty dishes heaped up. Sometimes it was one spoon unrinsed in the sink. The fury would last for hours. At last, he would go to bed and wait it out. Often he would fall asleep, drained by the intensity of his feelings.

When it passed, everything he had believed in his rage was revealed as fantasy, a trick of the light. He would cling to me and fervently rewind every word. To friends, he would say, in shell-shocked tones, 'I've been a pig to Sandy again.' Then there were promises: he would be calmer once he started acupuncture, when he started back swimming, when he got his new job.

With the rages came obsessions. Frustration with his failure to pass the driving test tormented him. Every few days he quit smoking, only to smoke again by nightfall. One week he bought an English Bull Terrier puppy, but the squirmy snub-nosed infant puppy yapped, tore things, and peed on the carpet; Rob took him to Battersea Dogs Home two days later. Everything was a compulsion. Either Rob could not do it or he could not stop.

The fighting went from bad to worse. It was every week, then every day until the dread of it came with waking. At last I was bearing a spleenish grudge against him. In the back of my mind, in a whisper, I considered leaving. Then I was picking fights with Rob myself, without knowing it.

The end was a fight like any other. He told me I didn't care about him, he snorted derisively at my protests. He picked up a book I'd left on the floor and threw it on the couch beside me, saying, 'Take that when you go' – clumsy melodramatic gestures that only hurt because they were gestures of hate. 'Get out of my flat,' he said, as he had said many times. 'Fuck off out of it now. You're poison.'

This time he never came to his senses. After forty-eight hours, I packed my bags and left.

The next week, Rob was back on drugs, and before too long he was dying again. Plain dying, in six months he lost three stone. He took someone out with him, a new girl-friend. Off crack three months, she had four kids in care. She was trying to straighten out and get them back when she met Rob. And she was a biker chick who'd worked the streets ten years, as hard as nails and helpless as a newborn.

Once Rob passed out too fast, hit concrete and broke his ankle. There were trips to the emergency room with overdoses. He was on crutches again, first from the broken ankle, then inanition and the doddery clumsiness of too much smack. The skin hung off his face; he looked old for the first time. Cassie upstairs saw Rob one day, took fright, and brought him cooked meals after that. Of his girlfriend, she said, 'She's like a female version of you, Rob,' awed.

Rob didn't tell me any of this at the time. He wasn't ready to spell out that he'd left me for the drugs, his first love. On the phone, he said he was depressed, yeah, but the job kept him sane. He was better off single. He got lonely, but it was just better. It was too painful to see me, Rob said, and sniffled and sounded hollow and distant. Of course I knew it all.

Unhappy ending

When one of us had a broken heart, Will used to put on
Gram Parsons and Emmylou Harris singing 'Love Hurts'
– a song so maudlin that we would be in stitches by the
second verse. If you listened to the words, the piling of
sentimentality upon self-pity became irresistibly silly. Our
suffering then seemed like part of an ancient tradition of
slushy stupidity, and we were in love with ourselves for
being part of it. We had done it exactly the way the song
said! It made you want to go dancing, and drink away your
troubles like a person in a song.

After I left Rob, I used to spend the night at Will's sometimes. He always made a great ceremony of dragging a
mattress into the front room, finding sheets that weren't
too filthy. He would play 'Love Hurts', and the Dylan songs
John Muckle used to play in Acton. In the morning, I would
wear Will's awful clothes sometimes; torn jeans and shirts
with paint stains, so unwashed they smelled like cattle and
felt muddy against the skin. I smoked Will's roll-ups and
was lost in an ecstasy of not trying to be a Published Author,
of letting myself be useless and unwanted and known.

I remember a particular night when Will and I made tea
in relays, talking and talking as the night outside wound
down to stillness. First it was his mate's divorce: 'He was
shagging the secretary. I ask you. Secretary-shagging, it lacks
all imagination, it's the pinnacle of fatness.' Then I had an
hour of Rob, then Will began on Richard Jones's new deb
wife to cheer me. 'She keeps saying she wants to buy me
clothes. You can't tell me that means nothing. She's *well*

cute.' We talked about growing older; Will swore 'I would still do you in a minute,' and nagged me into complimenting his youthful looks. His liver wasn't that clever, though, he said. His whole insides were shot. Never mind – die pretty. And at last, Will told me, trying to keep up the breezy tone, that he'd had a seizure.

He didn't remember it happening. He'd woken in hospital. 'Memory loss,' he said, pointing over his shoulder at the lost past. It had been a proper seizure, though; he was bruised head to foot.

I said, softly, scared, 'It was from the drinking?'

He said, 'Yah,' shrugged; then he met my eye and we shared fear. When he looked away, it was with all his weakness on the surface.

'So, how's not drinking going?' I said.

He made a face as if he'd tasted something foul. 'Ah, bollocks. I thought I could try to just drink less. Teetotal . . . I don't know.' He added gently, as if he were sharing his most private sorrow, 'Life gets boring.'

I gave him a look, I don't know, perhaps it was owlish. Some telltale grimace that made him burst out laughing, crowing, 'Fuck off! If there's one thing I won't stand for, it's people bloody *caring* about me. Creampuff!'

Here he suddenly halted, listened, and said, 'It's that bastard bird again. Cunt keeps fucking with my head, like it's really morning at 3 a.m. Cheep bloody cheep. Moralist!' Then he trailed towards his bedroom in fits and starts, commenting that it was a poor state of affairs when he didn't make a pass at me. He must be well fucked. No, it must be that he cared about me. 'People who *care about* people. I'm sensing a pattern. Must be stamped out.' No . . . he could tell I wasn't in a happy state, I didn't need his crap. 'Unless,' he said, from the doorway, lifting his chin with a mock-hopeful look, 'you really *needed* shagging?'

I smiled at him; I was already under the covers. I had picked my book up.

'Ooh,' he said, and cackled. 'The indifference . . . that's what hurts.'

And was gone. I lay back into the muddy-feeling sheets with my book and paused, like balancing on the idea that Will would start drinking again, and all that meant. (And Will was desiccated, had no meat on him now; his fears and pleasures had drunk him dry. In his cups, he had no short-term memory; any conversation looped. Sober, he was frightened by the missing days, the words that escaped him; life had begun to come to pieces in Will's hands. Then he was drinking to forget he'd pissed away his life and that his mind was going. He was drinking and not eating, Will was fading from himself and the volume was turned down, inexorably I lost my friend a little each time I saw him. I'd been telling him to stop drinking sixteen years then, sixteen years of wasted breath. There had even been a night when I was twenty, he was twenty-two, and I begged him on my knees, though it's hard to picture someone really begging on their knees, that's what I did, and I was crying. I was scared of seeing Will die some day.) He was going to die.

Then I couldn't bear that thought and opened my book.

It was another science fiction novel by the Strugatsky brothers. I had recently started reading in Russian again, from the same impulse of regression that made me love Will's seedy flat. I was hiding from the pressure of doing readings, meeting editors, being interviewed on radio; having to wear appropriate clothes and say the right thing. The book, entitled (loosely translated) *Snail Going Uphill*, was about a town where all the children develop amazing intellectual capacities, writing deathless poetry and mastering robotics, etc., at the age of ten. They are aided by shadowy figures who look like human adults but possess uncanny knowledge. The title referred to the concept that if a snail were climbing a hill, at any moment a human could see the poor labouring snail on its incline and lift it. In a few careless steps the lucky snail could be carried to the top, obviating the need to crawl.

At the end of the book, the children casually turn earth into a paradise using the force of their minds. Flowers sprout in their wake, etc. The protagonist is an adult who, given the chance to acquire the same powers, refuses because he would have to give up drinking.

Amos redux

I spent the day of Will's funeral with Amos. We took the train to Dorset and back together. Amos talked all the time about Julio Cortazar and topological logic, animated – not about Will. He was devising his relativistic economics then, which off the bat I took for crackpottery. When explained, though, it almost made sense.

Amos had been in and out of mental hospital for many years then. He had attempted suicide countless times in the fifteen years since we divorced. They were overdoses mainly, though there were also escapades with train tracks, head to the rail, the train squealing to a halt in the nick of time. It would be the inspiration of some psychotic dream; Samuel Beckett would command him, or his mother was overseeing a Stasi operation against his spirit, and only in death would it be safe. Or sometimes it was despair. Then there were spells in hospital, and lulls when he was sane, the medicated, diminished Amos who was gracious in the manner of a man who patiently bears an unhealing wound. In this mode, he was wonderful company. He'd acquired a genius for amiability, he had a tender humility that seemed inseparable from his impairment.

The day of Will's funeral we had an easy communion that cushioned me during the stiff Church of England ceremony, all hymn-singing and prayers. Will's mother even edited the speeches made by friends; they recalled his school days, then drifted into pretty generalities. The funeral programme featured a too-blonde photo of Will at eighteen. The print looked colourised and gave Will an expression he'd never had, a hair-tossing, carefree grin that made him look –

incongruously for him – gay. Meanwhile, Will was actually dead, and it was luxuriously consoling to have my Amos there, all tall and alive. It was the second to last time I saw Amos.

The last time, I went to his flat in Tottenham. We went up in the elevator which stank of bleach and urine. The flat had been wiped clean by his last madness, in which he had smashed his possessions and converted them into macabre sculptures. Now there was nothing but dirt, books scattered, a futon on the concrete floor. The toilet had no door at all. In one corner, there were stacks of the books he'd begun to publish, the poetry of psychotic writers. He had them printed cheaply in India. The first sample printing the Keralan printer showed him had floral patterns in the margins; the man thought that was how one should present poetry. I couldn't help feeling disappointed that Amos vetoed that idea.

I had begun having asthma at the time. The asthma gave me migraines, it was a bad year for me physically. That day I was having dizzy spells and shortness of breath. I had to perch on a wooden industrial spool, that was the only seating. That was when I told Amos about my plan to write a memoir. I said apologetically, 'It does have to mention our time together, somewhat.'

He was listening with narrowed eyes. When I finished my explanation, he said, '*I* remember nothing about our relationship, except the occasional catty outburst from you – completely unmotivated.'

I laughed but he looked down. I was having trouble breathing. I said, 'Oh, well.' (I would be saying, 'Oh, well,' a lot that year. It meant, all the people I love are dead. Even the ones who were alive presented themselves to me in their posthumous aspect: they will die too, all people are their own ghosts. They said to me, thinking of Amos sorrowfully, of Will, 'Oh, well.' And one of us would say at parting, sometimes, 'Don't die, will you?')

Then he took me to see the sculptures he'd been making: a lead Möbius strip that hung from the ceiling; a mounted seashell-and-string ladder which was a multilingual pun (a shell/*échelle*); an interlocking row of Bombay duck skulls, each with jaws wide open locked on the back of the skull in front, captioned DUCKEATDUCK, which I now own. Then I looked out the window on to the concrete balcony, accessible by a charmless security door. A fine blue wire mesh enclosed the balcony from the outside, obscuring the view. Two long rents had been cut in the mesh.

I knew right away. I said, cautiously, my voice very low with illness, 'What's that netting for? To keep pigeons out?'

Amos said, 'No, it's to stop people jumping off and killing themselves. Well, I wasn't having that!' He laughed, a rip-like cackle; and told me how he'd slashed the mesh with a knife when he was last insane.

I said, my head hurting and rushing, 'You know, it is to keep pigeons out. They shit all over the balcony and die there. John Muckle had it in Acton.'

Amos said, 'Sasha,' with reproach. He turned away, disappointed in me. We walked back out to the lift; I was too tired to breathe.

I later learned that Will, when he last visited Amos, said, 'Now you're better, let's get together one night and stitch those holes in the netting. We'll make it a ceremony. I don't like to see that, fuck it. I know you.' But Will died, of course, before they got to do it.

Amos threw himself from that twelfth-storey balcony to the concrete below: rest in peace is too pitiful, too thread-bare to say.

13

An Apparently Normal Human Adult

The Blue Button

I spent the Christmas after my divorce with Seth in
Washington DC. We were both sluggish with melancholy.
Seth was still undone by the death of Sheldon. Also, he and
Vita had split up. He would say, 'I don't know. I'm just a
sad sack nowadays.' Then he'd change the subject. He'd
say, 'I get so freaking depressed,' and change the subject.
Or, 'I just go to work and watch TV and go to sleep.'

His colleagues at the IRS were middle-aged people who
went home every night to their families. Seth didn't know
anyone in DC. He was living in an anonymous apartment
in a grim stand of high-rises stretching out of sight, because
the place was walking distance from his work. Although he'd
moved in months before, he used my visit for motivation
to finish unpacking.

For both of us, it was a time when being single seemed
like tragedy. The Christmas ads on TV hurt us with their
glib parade of happy families. I got flu and spent a day
stoned on NyQuil, watching looping reruns of *A Christmas
Story*, until when bedtime came, I was afraid to turn it off.
I'd insisted on cooking a real Christmas dinner, and then
it was sad to eat it.

I was also burdened, miseried, by my rift with my real

father. I was lost to him about this time, as if being carried out of earshot by a stubborn tide. It was a thing I fought and gave myself to gratefully by turns. And I might as well have hated him for all the hope there was that good would come of dialling his number in my unfaithful mood. Of course we are not dead, and life can take sharp corners. Even when we are dead, for all I know, we may be peaceable angels in the afterlife, who will commune and joke together on a cloudpuff, best of friends.

On Christmas Day, Seth and I drove out to Chesapeake Bay to scatter Sheldon's ashes in the water. Seth had been hanging onto these ashes for five years. In the car, we mostly listened to talk radio. We had had three days of each other's company, and now it was sweet to be in the clean air out of doors; to sit in a car while somebody did the talking for you.

As we pulled out of the city into the pretty deciduous forest around DC, though, Seth turned the radio down and said, 'Hey, Sandy. You remember "The Blue Button"?'

Both of us laughed.

'The Blue Button' was one of the first stories I ever wrote. At the beginning, the eponymous hero finds himself alone on a carpet. He is very, very lonely. The lonely carpet is described. There are no other buttons as far as the eye can see. How he wishes he had a friend! No – he is alone.

Then a person picks him up and puts him in a jar with many other buttons. He is contented. THE END.

I found it when we were looking through all my father's papers, the day before his funeral in West Palm Beach. Reading it, I started laughing and Seth looked up at me. So I read it aloud to Seth. He laughed so hard he fell onto his side; I was gasping the words and giggling. Diane heard us from the other room and came in curious. I read it again and all three of us laughed until we cried.

It was a moment of truce, like the Christmas football game between enemy troops in World War I. 'The Blue Button' could unite all people in fellowship. Or perhaps, in a brutal situation, any pretext for ceasefire makes one feel wild lovingkindness. Then, back to the trenches.

Seth told Vita about it later on. With her quaint, possibly Latvian, take on life, she decided it was a surefire hit. She would illustrate it. We would go into business together and make our fortune.

Now Seth said, 'Yeah, what were you, five or something, when you wrote that? You were a really smart kid.'

'Maybe six. I wasn't all that phenomenal. "The Blue Button" has its flaws.'

'You were pretty smart,' Seth said, laughing. 'I'm not saying you were an Einstein, but.'

'Well, I lost "The Blue Button".'

'Wha-at? Don't tell Vita that. She'd be heartbroken. Vita still asks about that book.'

'Really pretty lost.'

'That was the germ of a whole blockbuster children's series. Vita thinks so.'

'Yeah, in the sequel, the blue button meets a red button and falls in love.'

'And they have a purple button,' Seth said, without missing a beat, and we were laughing again.

As my laughter faded, the flu took. All the energy flowed out of me, and I was leaning my head against the car window smiling.

After a minute, I said, 'Seth? Did you ever want children?'

'I don't know,' he said, with an annoyed edge. 'Sure. But I'd have to meet someone. I don't know if that's going to happen.'

'Yeah, I have the same thing,' I said, as light-heartedly as I could. 'I guess it's just one of those things.'

'Yeah. After the way we grew up, with Mom in the hospital . . .' Seth took his hands off the steering wheel to turn his palms up helplessly. Then he was steering again and saying, 'Kind of scared of relationships.'

'There was Vita,' I said cautiously.

'*That* ended.' Seth shrugged. 'Don't ask me.'

'I should be more scared.'

'I guess!'

I wanted to laugh at that, but he wasn't smiling. I bit my lip. Then the woods and the houses seemed to sink back into the ground to bare the Chesapeake Bay, a vista of watery light to the edge of the world. Intense blue diamonds floated deep in an ocean of translucent flowing; and the bridge ran across it in a leaping shape. I saw a shorebird tip above, before the car turned and it was snatched out of sight. I wanted to say, 'Not for us the purple buttons,' or something corny, except that I wanted it to be all right. Then Seth turned the radio up.

At last

I got out of the car and stood with my face to the wind while Seth got the ashes from the trunk. We were in a nondescript parking lot, haunted by a gleam and fishiness from the water, which was hidden by a stand of trees. There were no other cars. It was sunny, only cold when the wind pulled hard.

The ashes were in a small black plastic box. A form was Scotch taped to the side with the name of the deceased and the funeral home's name and address typed into blanks. When Seth opened the box, the ashes themselves were in a clear plastic bag inside. The ashes were pale and fine; on the plastic, they moved like a liquid.

We walked down to the end of a dock. There I got out a book of Jewish prayers we'd found and opened to the mourning prayer we'd chosen. He read aloud, then I read aloud, and though I wanted to invest the words with significance, they remained just words, sounding small, mundane, in the wind coming over the bay.

We took turns shaking the ashes out. The wind was strong enough that it was difficult to stop them blowing back onto the dock; we had to bend down near the waves. As the ashes touched the water, they vanished.

Finally the ashes were all gone. Seth put his hand on my shoulder.

There was a Mexican family laughing coming down to the shore as we walked up from the shore. When they saw us they all stopped talking.

Then we drove back to the city with the radio playing.

* * *

The memory of your life, dear father, rises before me this solemn moment as I stand before your grave and recall all the years of unselfish devotion, kindness, love and encouragement which you have shown me during your life. I recall all the sacrifices you made for my welfare, and the many comforts with which you provided me. The passing of time will never diminish the blessed memories of your life.